For Susie

Whom Father Would Have Liked

# ONE

FATHER had a beard like Ulysses S. Grant; he was short and fat, too. He always wore the kind of a tie Abraham Lincoln wore. All through my childhood I thought of Father in terms of great and heroic men—and with reason.

Just to survive my escapades required more than one man's—one ordinary man's—courage. But I had four escapade-ish brothers and one escapade-ish sister. And it wasn't just his own family for whom my Father had concern. Actually, his family was the whole of Zanesville, Ohio. Fortunately, my Father was ingenious. Too bad he wasn't omniscient and omnipotent. It would have made things a bit easier for him.

"You're not only Jewish," Father said to me whenever I'd done something wrong, and that was often, "but you're my son. You must set an example. Everybody expects it of you."

Father was the Orthodox rabbi in Zanesville. It was strange that my criminal career should be connected with his synagogue.

Behind the House of God was a little house marked Men and Women. It was this little house

1

that was to be used as a temporary warehouse for stolen goods.

The synagogue was big, sprawling, without architectural design. All that labeled it a place of worship was the circular stained-glass window over the door. A multicolored Star of David ornamented that window.

This was four years after the flood of 1913. The synagogue had been in the flood, but several years were yet to go by before it was repainted.

Whenever possible Father would refer to the color of the synagogue as a "beautiful Muskinggum River brown." He didn't mean the "beautiful." He wanted to make the people ashamed of themselves for permitting the synagogue to wear its flood color.

I don't remember the burial of the prayer books and holy articles damaged by the flood. But Father often talked about it. The water-mutilated *sefer-torahs* were placed in the ground of the cemetery with all the tragic sadness attending a loved one's death.

What I remembered very vividly, however, were the boxes of chocolate that floated out of Bloomer's Candy Company. Sy and Mott, my older brothers, and Sophie, my sister, and I went wading for them when the flood waters receded. Some of the candy wasn't even damp; it all tasted good.

2

Being in the flood district, the synagogue was in a semimanufacturing district. The side of the street it was on was strictly residential, but across the street was an ice-cream factory, Dockray's Brass and Iron Foundry, and Frank's Hides and Fertilizers. The secular and profane across the street from the Holy of Holies was a constant disturbance to Father. It took him all of ten years scheming and prodding to remedy this wrong, to have a new pressed-brick edifice erected, and in a neighborhood devoid of foundry hammerings and fertilizer smells.

But I was Father's immediate problem. I'd become a thief.

One of Father's favorite sermons was the "never take the easy path, but always take the hard path" sermon. It seemed like utterly foolish advice. But this was Father in a sermon, and I felt that Father outside of a sermon was much smarter.

It started with a little thing—just as Father warned evil things always do. I sold the *Cleveland Plain Dealer* and the *Chicago Tribune* in addition to the *Zanesville Sunday News*. Each Sunday I stole three funny sheets, one from each of the different papers I sold.

Lefty O'Rourke, who was four years older than I and wrote with his left hand and had an extra little toe on his right foot, was someone to be greatly admired. That was why I bragged to him about stealing the funny sheets.

3

Lefty made a derisive sound—he blew and let his relaxed tongue vibrate.

"You don't know what real swiping is," he boasted. "You're just the Jew rabbi's kid."

I was hurt. I edged my chest up closer to Lefty. "I can swipe anything you can swipe. There!"

"How could you swipe anything. Funnies are all you kin swipe. Your old man's the Jew preacher, ain't he?"

To be thought inadequate because of my relation to Father's sissy profession was simply awful. The boys of the neighborhood were always thinking that too. So I knew that once and for all I had to prove there was not an ecclesiastical fiber in me. I had to be as wicked as King Pharaoh. And never must I set an example for the community, as Father always insisted I do.

The following Saturday afternoon, on a dare, I went out with Lefty to steal things from a five-and-ten.

Lefty and I approached a candy counter.

Since it was Saturday—the Sabbath—I was dressed in my best suit. Lefty wasn't very personable, however. His cap was a greasy-black. The snap on the bill wasn't fastened, and the cap was pulled back in Apache style. Lefty's pale face wasn't clean either, and his black eyes were constantly in furtive motion.

Lefty's hands were as quick as his eyes. Chocolate bars were on the counter one moment, and in

4

that very same moment they were in his pocket.

My hands couldn't begin to move toward a candy bar. They were hands descendant from a long line of rabbis and pious men.

Lefty went from the candy counter, his pockets bulging, to the toy counter. His hands went out and then a toy was under his coat. I stood by, wretched because I couldn't steal, frightened because I was certain to be arrested for having stolen.

Outside, Lefty didn't say anything. Worse, he crushed my heart by blowing and making his tongue vibrate derisively.

I still had to impress Lefty and it was for that reason I suggested using the synagogue's outhouse as a temporary repository for Lefty's swag. He filled my pockets. Then he went back into the five-and-ten for another load. When he came out, bulging opulently, we hurried down alleys to the synagogue.

"You're no good swiping," Lefty remarked with finality as we emptied our pockets.

We put the candy and toys on the toilet bench, placing them carefully so nothing would fall through the two round holes.

"Yuh watch the stuff," Lefty said. "I'll be back soon with some more."

Lefty went. I wanted to tell him not to go, but I knew if I did, my reputation would be ruined.

I couldn't sit down because the candy and

5

toys were on the toilet bench. I stood and waited for Lefty's return. I had the door latched, but that did not give me much of a feeling of security. It also made the little outhouse dark.

The darkness aided my imagination. I saw Lefty caught in the act of dropping a chocolate bar into his pocket, Lefty dragged outside by the collar, Lefty implicating me to save himself.

But a laden Lefty returned. He rewarded me generously—a green, striped balloon, which when blown up had the size and appearance of a watermelon, and he also gave me a box of marshmallows and two bars of chocolate. Participate with him next week, and he promised that I'd get a greater share of the profits.

The following Saturday I accompanied Lefty on his stealing trip. I really writhed with fear this time, because Lefty said, "Your wrists ain't broke. You might as well do some of the takin', too."

But I didn't get a chance to do "some of the takin'." Lefty had an off day. The very first candy he put his hands on, he dropped. Lefty told me afterwards that that was no cause for alarm. He could have casually picked the candy from the floor and put it back on the counter, as if it had fallen by accident.

I was panicky, however; keyed up to a sprinter's tenseness by the knowledge that on that day I was to make my debut as a thief. I ran for the door. Lefty had no choice but to follow. We bumped a few innocent shoppers, but we got out of that five-and-ten before you could say store detective.

I expected Lefty to punch me in the nose after telling me what he thought of me. But he was very patient. Very understanding.

"It was just buck fever," Lefty said sagely. "It'll hit the best of 'em."

I wasn't so sure about that. I thought there must be something seriously wrong with me. I wasn't like Lefty.

The next day at Sunday School my attention perked up in anomalous fashion. Father was saying something about the iniquity of the fathers being visited upon the children to the third and fourth generations.

That meant my children would suffer because of what I was doing on Saturday afternoons in the five-and-ten.

I raised my hand. "You mean if we do something like—like fighting in the street that . . ."

"When you grow up," Father finished, "your children will be punished for what you've done. Exactly."

I became very silent. I reasoned that Father's grandparents must have done something extremely evil for my father to have been cursed by having me. This whole matter of posterity-punishment was fascinating. Subconsciously it was to serve as a justification for my not going out with Lefty on his Saturday afternoon shopping tours. It was a delightful, face-saving rationalization.

I usually fell asleep right after supper, my head resting on the round dining-room table, but I remember I didn't that Sunday night.

My extreme interest in that morning's Sunday School lesson perplexed and pleased Father. He talked to me about remorse. I recognized a lot of his Rosh Hashonah sermon in it.

"Gee," I said. "Just feeling sorry for what you've done. That's easy."

Mother stopped long enough on her way to the kitchen to say, "That boy's been up to something."

"What have you done, Willie?" Father asked. By this time he'd become suspicious too.

"Oh, nothing," I said. "Nothing."

Before the following Saturday arrived, I told Lefty I couldn't steal any more. I went into a lengthy explanation.

Lefty just blew around his relaxed tongue and let it vibrate derisively.

I didn't care. Father's religion was all right, I thought. It was wonderful to know I didn't have to steal anymore.

## TWO

No matter what Father might do, no matter how deeply he jumped into predicaments by doing good, I was always on his side. My championing him was inevitable; he was so clearly, so poignantly an underdog.

Prayer is an expression of humility and Father was always praying.

Every morning upon arising Father put on phylacteries and prayed for at least an hour. I was supposed to do the same. But there were times that I "forgot." I would eat breakfast without having said my morning prayers. And according to the rules, one could not say morning prayers after one had eaten. I knew this rule and made the most of it.

"You forget to pray," Father would say scornfully. "But you don't forget to eat, do you?"

I heard that rebuke, couched in exactly the same words, hundreds of times. Father was a patient man; I, a consistent sinner.

I did not forget to eat because eating tasted good—it was sensory, pleasantly tangible. Prayer was unintelligible words keeping me from play.

Still, I marveled at Father's praying capacity.

Father would often say—and it was almost a boast—that not once did he fail to say a prayer before eating the different foods of a meal.

For quite some time, I made a game out of watching Father at meals to see if he might forget to say the blessings. He did not say them out loud, but his lips moved and I watched his lips.

One Monday at lunch time I was certain I caught Father eating bread without first blessing God—acknowledging Him to be the maker of bread.

I remember it was a Monday, because Mother was conventional in all things and washed clothes on Monday.

The kitchen was foggy with steam. Mother boiled the clothes in the process of cleaning them. And lunch wasn't ready because Mother had been busy with the clothes.

"I see we're having boiled underwear for lunch," Father said, hunger making him irritable.

"In just two minutes I'll have something ready for you," Mother answered. "The world's not coming to an end."

"You shouldn't start washing clothes around noontime."

Father was really arguing against Mother's washing clothes. He didn't like the idea that Mother, already overworked, had to wash clothes, too.

"Who tells you to do the washing?" he'd often ask Mother.

He knew he couldn't afford to have the washing sent out. Yet by asking Mother that question, he implied that it was Mother who chose to do the washing and that if it were up to him she most certainly would not wash clothes. It made those steamy Mondays easier for Father to bear.

Mother put the tablecloth on the table on this particular Monday. I watched as she smoothed it out with her hands.

Next she placed a plate of bread in the center of the table.

Father, to prove his hunger and anger graphically, took a slice of bread and tore a savage bite from it.

I was watching Father. Out of habit, I watched his lips before he bit angrily into the bread. They hadn't moved in prayer.

It was all a game. I was elated that Father had forgotten to pray and I'd caught him at it.

"You didn't that time!" I screamed, and I pointed at Father.

Father glared. "What? What are you talking about?"

"You forgot to say . . ." and I rattled off the blessing for bread.

"Why do you bother my head?"

"But you forgot. And you said you never forget."

Mother came to Father's rescue. In her hand,

she had the sawed-off broomstick she used for lifting and stirring the boiling wash.

I'd asked her many times to let me use it on the wash. Once she told me that it would be all right for me to use the stick when I grew a few more inches in height. All the other times she just said a very plain and adult "no."

And now Mother handed me the stick. I didn't ask her what had made her change her mind; I rushed to the kitchen range and the boiling wash.

For some time, for years, I thought about Father forgetting to say the blessing for the bread that day. I was certain he had forgotten. I knew that whenever Father said, "Don't bother my head," he no longer had a logical leg to stand on or to kick me with. Stuck, he resorted to the brute force of dismissal.

It occurred to me that Father might have said the blessing in his heart. But I knew he hadn't, for I knew what Father thought of that kind of praying. It served too well as a device for not praying at all. Father had only scorn for those who spoke of prayers of the heart.

"A prayer not put into words," Father often said, "is like a house without roof or walls."

Actually prayer was only an incidental part of Father's life. He'd pray, but then hustle out and do the things you'd expect a praying man to do.

There was the case of me and the smiling librarian.

The time arrived when I was old enough to take out a library card. The thought of approaching the librarian and telling her what I wanted was frightening. She was old and skinny and around her neck wore what looked like a strip torn from the bottom of a lace curtain.

Her elaborate smile gave me courage, however.

During the course of jotting down my name, address, and so on, she said, "You're Jewish, aren't you?" And before I could answer, she added, "That's all right."

I told Father what she'd said and what a nice woman she was and how beautifully she smiled. But Father was strangely angry. "I'll have a talk with her," Father said. "I must tell her how happy I am that she approves of your being Jewish."

Father certainly was a hard one for a child to understand.

And I was always puzzled why prayer, since he did so much of it, didn't help Father more than it did. Salesmen could sell him anything.

It was easy to tell when Father had bought something he knew he shouldn't have. He smiled like a child, shyly hiding its head against its mother. It was his defense. How could you throw hard words at him when he was so innocent and helpless?

My oldest brother, Sy, threw plenty the day Father bought the secondhand Chevrolet.

"What do you know about automobiles?" Sy demanded.

"The salesman told me it was in A-1 condition."

"Naturally. You think salesmen have scruples?"

"But, my boy, you must learn to trust people. This salesman was telling the truth. I could see he had an honest face."

It then came out that Father hadn't even listened to the car's motor. He'd liked the appearance of the car; the appearance of the salesman's face.

Sy ranted. He said Father was naive and gullible. He said with great scorn that Father bought the car because it was a Chevrolet, and since we'd never had more than a Ford, this lifted us up one notch socially.

It was all very true; but paradoxically, Father's foibles were also his virtues.

The Chevrolet, motor-unheard, turned out to be a very good car. It never gave us any serious trouble. Whenever we'd speak of how well the car was behaving, Father would smile and say, "You see, people are all right after all. Salesmen, too."

Uncannily, salesmen got the scent of Father and the little money he had. If Father answered the door, they were certain of a sale. Mother, on the other hand, was able to open the front door an inhospitable crack and shake her head.

"I feel sorry for them," Father told Mother defensively. "They have to make a living. Going from door to door. It's not easy."

That was the time Father bought the Homiletic Commentary set. The salesman assured Father that those thirty-two volumes would aid him immeasurably in the preparation of his sermons. They were blue, and the title and volume number were in gold letters.

The After Dinner Speeches set was red and in gold letters. The Shakespeare set was also red and in gold letters. The Babylonian Talmud was green, the letters in gold.

The furniture salesmen appeared and talked to Father after the book salesmen were through with him. Bookcases were necessary to house the books, they said. Father bought sectional bookcases. The idea of buying additional sections—as he needed them—appealed to Father.

"Soon you'll be putting bookcases in my kitchen," Mother prophesied on numerous occasions. The tone of her voice made it clear that her exaggeration was meant as reprimand.

The climax of Father's gullibility arrived with a stranger by the name of Johnson Becker. Becker, according to his nonengraved card, was both a manufacturer and a financier.

Becker and his doings were to take a worthy place beside the legends of our family: the one about a relative of ours who committed suicide by jumping off London Bridge on the night he was to have been married; Mr. Meisels who ran away with the few dollars that constituted Father's monetary wealth.

My brothers, sister and I liked best the one of the man who jumped off London Bridge.

"Why'd he do it?" I once asked Mother.

My brothers and sister chimed in, "Why? Tell us why . . ."

"The poor fellow must have thought it an easier plunge than marriage," Father said, and laughed.

Mother wouldn't talk, however. And I could tell by the way she looked at Father that it wasn't something to laugh about; and, like coffee, it wasn't for children.

But Mother didn't mind telling the Mr. Meisels story over and over again, however. We had a picture of Mr. Meisels, too. He had posed with a teacup held daintily in one hand. In his other hand, resting against his thigh, was a pipe.

I studied the picture often during my childhood. This man couldn't have been a robber, I told myself. He had an elegant mustache, and his high collar was old-fashioned, but it was also elegant. Of course I didn't realize this was the elegance of a fop and a confidence man.

So Mother told the Mr. Meisels story and had his picture always accessible. Father knew why she told it so often. She wanted him never to forget what a fool he'd been to have given Mr. Meisels all his money—three hundred and fifty dollars—to invest in a furniture store on South Seventh Street. Mr. Meisels flew the coop, of course, the money Father had given him tucked under his wing.

To understand what happened when Mr. Johnson Becker came to town, you must understand how my father felt about Zanesville. It was his town; the relationship a paternal one. The welfare of all its people and the town itself was his personal concern.

Father had had other congregations. In England, before coming to this country—Blackpool, Newcastle upon Tyne. And he was rabbi for short periods in Butler, Pennsylvania, and Danville, Virginia.

I'd heard Father speak of all these places, and somehow I always had the feeling Father regarded them as steps toward Zanesville and nothing more.

One spring day as I was just leaving for school, Mr. Johnson Becker rang our doorbell.

I answered the door.

"Is the rabbi at home?" a voice, deep and resonant with dignity, asked.

"No. Not right now. No—but he'll be home soon though."

The man's regal, affluent appearance rattled me. He wasn't Father's usual type of caller. Poor,

17

little people—wanting a meal or a place to spend the night—were Father's visitors as a rule and there was scarcely ever an exception.

"I don't mind waiting," the man was saying, his extreme amiability causing him to bow slightly at the waist.

Mother came up behind me just then, and took over. She told me if I didn't hurry I'd be late for school again.

I hurried, but I daydreamed, too. Daydreamed about the tall, erect, gray-haired man who'd come to call on Father.

The school hall was very quiet. Terribly, ominously quiet. That quiet had become synonymous in my mind with being late.

I didn't lie to my teacher, as she confronted me, to get out of being punished. My imagination simply told the only truth it knew.

"A man—a Senator—came to see my father," I told the teacher to explain my tardiness. "It was like a geography lesson," a civics lesson was what I meant, "just to hear him talk."

Thus I proved my lateness to have been educational, worthwhile. The teacher was without rebuttal.

That night at the supper table, I was surprised to learn that Mr. Johnson Becker was not a Senator. He was a manufacturer of carpets and a financier.

"He has more money than he knows what to do with," Father said.

"Is that what a financier is?" I asked.

Father laughed. "Yes." He laughed some more. "Yes, I suppose so."

Father then passed Mr. Johnson Becker's card around the supper table. The name was in bold-faced type. Under it were the words "manu-facturer" and "financier." They were in italics. The concept of a calling card impressed the entire family, everyone but Mother.

"You'd think the card was an idol," Mother sniffed, "the way you look at it."

"It's not the card," Father said. "But you know that Mr. Becker actually wants to start a carpet factory here? You know what that will mean for Zanesville?"

"You're the rabbi. Starting carpet factories isn't your business."

"Everybody's business is my business. You know that."

"Let's eat our supper and not talk about carpet factories."

Mother thus put a period to the discussion. She was fearful of any arguments at the dining table. An uncle of hers died of stomach ulcers and, as Mother put it, "he spent more time arguing at meal times than eating."

But there is a great deal of time between meals. And between meals, in the days that followed, Mother told Father what she thought of Mr. Johnson Becker. He was another Mr. Meisels.

19

"Just look at this picture," Mother said, thrusting the picture of Mr. Meisels toward Father. "They even look alike. Meisels and this tall, white-haired thief."

"Mr. Becker's a gentleman. He . . ."

"Why? Because he acts like one? And what kind of a name is Johnson Becker anyhow. The two names match like a brown egg and a white egg. I'll bet his real name is a different one altogether."

I enjoyed listening to Father and Mother. Their arguments frightened me. But this was clearly not an argument, merely verbal sport.

Fortunately Sy was away at college. I was glad, because I was sure he'd have sided with Mother. My sister Sophie and Bob and Dave, my younger brothers, agreed with me that Father was right and that Mother was wrong.

Father felt obliged to convince Mother that Mr. Johnson Becker's integrity was of the purest. He had to have Mr. Becker on the scene to do this, and so he insisted that Mr. Becker have his meals at our house.

In spite of Mother's antagonism, she dressed up the evening Mr. Becker had his first dinner with us. She justified her preparation of meals for the man, by saying that otherwise he'd have had to eat in a restaurant.

The first words Mr. Becker said to Mother that evening he came to dinner were, "What a beautiful brooch you're wearing."

The compliment splashed Mother's face with a pleased-pink. "It's an heirloom," she said. "My mother gave it to me. And when Sophie gets married, I'll hand it on to her."

Sophie giggled.

I cut off the giggle by yanking on one of Sophie's pigtails. "Ding, ding," I said as I yanked. Sophie started to cry; there was more whine than pain or sadness in it. I was surprised that Mother didn't make me leave the table.

As the meal progressed, I understood the basis for her leniency.

Mr. Johnson Becker's gallant manner had Mother engrossed. Every dish she served was decorated the next moment by a compliment. He'd never tasted anything that the gods couldn't have eaten with equal relish. The *holashkes* were just like his mother made them. And before he left that evening he again marveled at the beauty of Mother's brooch. Flattery and Mr. Becker had caused Mother to surrender unconditionally.

The tomorrows after that were progressively more exciting. Zanesville, Father was sure, would become as big as Columbus, the state capital; Becker's carpet factory would do that for Zanesville. Mother still didn't speak in favor of the factory. But instead of opposing it, she now remained silent.

But she did speak of Mr. Johnson Becker.

He had compared her cooking to the cooking of his mother.

"When a man speaks well of his mother," she said, looking at me with an emphasizing stare, "that man is all right."

And Father didn't tire of telling the Henry Ford story. He'd heard it from Charlie Rolands, secretary of the Chamber of Commerce. Father had introduced Mr. Becker to Rolands and that was when he heard the story.

It seems that Henry Ford had come to Zanesville with the intention of opening up an automobile factory. There were no backers available, however. The automobile was regarded by the citizenry as a noisy, unpredictable buggy, appealing only to the flashy, gambling element of the community. Ford shook his head and proceeded to Detroit, for he didn't think the horse was here to stay.

Father found a text for a sermon in this error that Zanesville had once made. Fear has only eyes in the back of its head was the text. He preached on it one Friday night. Everybody began whispering during the sermon, for though Father dressed up the story of Henry Ford in the colorful patterns of a parable it was plain Father was telling the people to accept progress via the carpet factory and Mr. Johnson Becker.

Mother gave it to Father—and vehemently— all the way home from the synagogue. Father always kept a step ahead of Mother when they were walking in the street—and now, with reason, he tried to keep several steps ahead. Fury helped Mother keep up with him. They were walking so quickly I had to dog-trot to be sure I wouldn't miss anything.

"They're right," Mother was saying. "You've no business selling a carpet factory from the pulpit. I thought you had more sense."

"I didn't mention a carpet factory."

"No. But the carpet factory stuck out all over. Your sermon-words didn't hide it."

Father slowed down, puffing. He was too heavy-set for simultaneous fast walking and argumentation. Walking slowly now, his mood softened. He smiled as he took Mother's arm. "I'm glad they understood what I was talking about," he admitted. "Glad."

"You won't be so glad when you have to go looking for another position."

"I was afraid they'd not understand. Just think I was talking in abstractions." Mother had pulled her arm away, but Father took it again. "You don't begin to realize how good it feels to tie a sermon to something big—and real . . ."

"Big and real!" Mother freed her arm again. "A carpet factory!" She looked as if she'd just sampled soup she'd forgotten to season with salt.

The next night—it was a Saturday night— two storms broke. One was filled with spring thunder and lightning; the other with roiling emotions.

The proprietor of the Zanesville Royal Hotel came tramping and sputtering into our house. His umbrella, turned inside out, was a metal skeleton in a shroud of torn black cloth.

Where was this Mr. Johnson Becker, the hotel man wanted to know. He enunciated Mr. and Johnson and Becker clearly and distinctly. All his hate was focused momentarily in saying the man's name in just the way he said it.

Sophie, Bob, and I hung fearfully at the periphery of the scene.

At just that moment, Mother came screaming from the bedroom, her arms lifted in alarm. "My brooch! My brooch!"

Father whirled from the tiny man with the shattered umbrella to the more pressing problem of Mother.

"My brooch is gone," Mother was sobbing now. "I put it in the top chiffonier drawer. I remember . . ."

Father at that moment was going through the steps of a deduction. He must have been thinking: Mr. Johnson Becker liked that brooch very much; he'd said so many times. Mr. Johnson Becker is gone and so is the brooch; the two of them could have gone off together.

Sophie started to cry. I yanked at her pigtails to make her stop; but that didn't turn off her voice, it only increased the volume.

"Now when I get married I won't get the

brooch," Sophie blubbered and slobbered. "Well, I won't get married then. I'm not going to."

Father took a second to turn to Sophie and say, "Quiet," and then he turned back to Mother and the little man from the Royal Hotel.

As backdrop to all this was a furious display of spring lightning and thunder.

I saw that Father's beard was a dark-brown frame to his pallor.

"Can it all be a hoax?" he asked the room. "The carpet factory? Everything? But why?"

The next day—and its events—answered Father's questions.

Johnny Riker barged in during breakfast. Massive and blustering, Riker ran the meat market that served the Jewish families in Zanesville.

Riker shouted that he'd been cashing checks for Johnson Becker; not a single one, he'd just learned, was worth the ink with which it was forged. He'd thought manufacturer Becker a right fellow to do a favor for; he had no idea he was a crook.

It was hard for Johnny Riker to make this indictment without using his swearing vocabulary —a vocabulary of scholarly length. But Riker wouldn't swear in Father's presence.

Riker's face was a purple-red. The color of his indignation blended with his groping for words respectable enough for my father to hear.

When Johnny Riker first came in, I was afraid he was going to upset the table and the breakfast on it. I'd heard the story of how once he'd come home from the slaughter house to find his wife had prepared a meatless dinner. "No meat!" he'd bellowed accusingly. And he'd tipped over the table with a violent heave so that all the food and dishes on it went crashing to the floor.

Father didn't get to do any work that morning on his Saturday sermon. Johnny Riker had been the vanguard of a stream of furious people, all of them cheated in some way by Johnson Becker. Several women told of having lent Becker money. Weakened by his grand appearance, they had readily succumbed to his flattery.

I remember the sermon that Saturday. Father hadn't had time, because of all that had happened, to prepare one. His sermon was consequently extemporaneous, very current and taken from life. Man made plans, Father said, and God destroyed. Man put his trust in princes and Mammon.

There was more of spanking than consolation in the sermon. Everybody in the synagogue seemed to be groaning or looking at the floor or ceiling.

That Saturday afternoon Sophie cried for quite some time about the brooch that would have been hers if Mr. Johnson Becker had not taken a fancy to it. Her face a very ripe and very sad persimmon.

The brooch was very beautiful. A delicate cameo. Held to the light, it took on the gentle luminosity of a dawn sky.

But Mother told Sophie to stop her crying, and to teach her and Father a lesson: "If you're going to get married, you'll need more than that brooch. You'll need a decent, hard-working man." Then Mother looked scornfully at Father. "You'll need a man who's not too trusting."

But Mother realized she'd also been taken in by Mr. Johnson Becker. From that time on, she no longer showed Father the picture of Mr. Meisels when Father showed signs of being gullible. It would have been a picture pinching her foot, too.

# ⌘⌘⌘⌘⌘⌘THREE⌘⌘⌘⌘⌘⌘

MOTHER always said, "You'll *never* learn."

Father would nod and smile. Mother's prediction didn't bother Father because he intended going on and on meddling.

Father described himself as "the little fool who marries them and buries them."

But Mother was right when she said Father spent more time at meddling than he spent at weddings and funerals. Meddling was what he enjoyed. Weddings and funerals meant the preparation of a speech; and sitting down and writing speeches or sermons in his big canvas-back ledgers was something Father did not enjoy.

Of course when his meddling resulted in a wedding, he had to pay for the pleasure he'd had by writing a speech. Later, if it were a boy, he had to pay the extra toll of a circumcision speech.

There was no speech involved in the Mrs. Greenberg transaction, however. No speech— wedding, funeral, or circumcision.

Mrs. Greenberg lived alone in a cottage that slanted on its foundations as though it were being blown by the wind. That erratic aspect of her house made it just the right house for Mrs. Greenberg. It matched the weird look in her green eyes, the gnarled leanness of her old body.

The kids in the neighborhood—I among them —would follow her like a cloud of gnats chanting, "Greenberg with the green eyes, the green eyes, the green eyes . . ."

She took futile swats at us. The chanting merely crescendoed, became unmistakably sadistic.

No wonder poor Mrs. Greenberg suspected the bank teller's civil, sincere "good morning." No wonder she saw treachery in his smile.

Mrs. Greenberg trusted Father, however. He was the only friend she had. As a dog will trust one person and not another, so she trusted Father. And so she came and told Father about the bank teller.

Father took her into the living room; he didn't want her to think she wasn't being treated as company. I followed furtively, fearful lest Mrs. Greenberg had come to tell Father I had been among those who molested her.

Tears rolled down her cheeks and she blew her nose into her hand, then wiped her hand on her dress. "I told them to keep the money," she sobbed. " 'Good morning,' the bank man said. I saw him smile. He didn't think I saw, but I did. I know what he was thinking. 'Oh oh, Mrs. Greenberg. She's come for her money already.' "

"They don't care if you take your money out,"

29

Father said. He put his hand on her shoulder to calm her.

" 'Keep the money,' I said. 'I don't want it.' I saw him smile. I know what he was thinking."

Father tried to reason with Mrs. Greenberg, but she didn't seem to hear what he said.

"It looks like I'll have to withdraw her money," Father told Mother that night at the supper table.

"Of course," Mother said.

"But she's a poor woman. She needs the money. And if I don't . . ."

"You'll *never* learn. *Never*."

I went down to the bank with Father.

While Father talked to the president of the bank on the other side of a mahogany fence, I wandered about the bank lobby. That was how I happened to find the hundred-dollar bill. It was on the floor, in full view, and right under the teller's cage.

I brought it to Father and the bank president immediately. The bank president took the bill. He smiled down at me from behind his majestic gray mustache.

"You've a mighty fine boy there," he said to Father, placing a benedictive hand on my head.

That was all the reward I received. I complained to Father afterwards. Father agreed with me that Mr. Irwell, the bank president, should have given me some concrete evidence of his gratitude.

"He had an obligation, and he avoided it,"

Father said. "If he had given you a chocolate ice-cream cone, for example, you'd have a higher regard for honesty than you have now."

Father bought me the ice-cream cone.

Father also took me to Mrs. Greenberg's house —which turned out even more of a reward.

Curiosity had made me eager to see the inside of Mrs. Greenberg's home. It was the next best thing to a gingerbread house. Its wind-blown slant gave it its fairy-tale quality.

There were fourteen cats in the house; four overflowed onto the porch. I counted them as Father roamed the house looking for Mrs. Greenberg. The front door was open and so was the back, but there was no Mrs. Greenberg.

Father sensed right from the start that Mrs. Greenberg was gone for good. He somehow understood how deeply she'd been hurt by the bank teller's friendly "Good morning."

And Mrs. Greenberg had vanished. She was gone with the suddenness and completeness of a light switched off. Vanished as Mr. Johnson Becker had vanished. Gone as Lefty O'Rourke, that depleter of five-and-tens, was gone from my life when he was sent to the reformatory at Mansfield for stealing a bicycle.

I was troubled by Mrs. Greenberg's disappearance, feeling I was partially responsible. If I and the others hadn't tormented her for having green eyes, maybe she wouldn't have left.

Her departure, however, was not without its

advantages. The sixteen dollars and twenty-four cents, which constituted her bank account and which Father had withdrawn, was used by Father for minor charities. Mother permitted us to have three of the fourteen cats.

"There are still eleven cats," Father said hesitantly. "Someone must take care of them."

"Don't look at me!" Mother snapped.

Little Sophie was growing up. "I know a lot of families who want kittens," she said. A business scheme was rotating in her head.

Father gave her permission to find homes for the eleven cats.

If people would pay money for the cats, Sophie reasoned, they'd take better care of them. It was something of a rationalization, for, at the moment, she needed a quarter. There was a doll in a store on Main Street toward which she'd developed a maternal affection.

She held an outdoor, public cat sale, after telling her friends at school about it. Ten of the cats went at two cents apiece. A tomcat, with a surly, gray moon-face, brought a nickel. Sophie had her quarter. Twenty minutes later she had her doll.

Father smiled when Sophie told him about it.

"Some good has come from Mrs. Greenberg's going," Father said musingly. "Through compensation, God is kind to his children."

Father always said things like that, things we couldn't begin to understand. But he'd just finished

Emerson's essay on compensation. A salesman had sold Father a ten-volume set of Emerson.

We weren't the only ones who didn't understand Father. And Mother wasn't the only one who accused him of meddling.

"Praying's your job," Lou Weiss, president of the congregation, told Father categorically.

Weiss owned the movie theatres in town. He was extrovert broad; his jowls warned one of his power and efficiency. He didn't believe in "risky propositions." And Father's participation in a nonsectarian Thanksgiving Day Service at the Memorial Hall was definitely a risky proposition.

There was extra grumbling against Father after the Johnson Becker carpet factory hoax. Father heard it, but it didn't stir up his calm. It agitated Mother, however.

And Father almost always caused trouble to descend upon himself by his collaborations with Cupid. He was everlastingly bringing boys and girls together, with matrimony the objective.

Father really took the verse in Genesis very seriously, about a man needing a woman and a woman needing a man. If he hadn't, he never would have attempted to make the match which involved Butler, Pennsylvania, his former pulpit, and Zanesville.

Father had had his hand in many a local romance. Here was one that crossed state boundaries. The spatial scope of the project appealed to Father.

"It'll make for good will between Zanesville and Butler," Father said.

Mother said, "Sure." She said it too readily to have meant sure.

Father caught on. "Well, don't you think it's about time that Leone Smith got married?"

"Everyone thinks so. Leone most of all."

"So what's wrong? The Wexler boy will be perfect for her."

"You call him a boy? When you're as old as he is you're no longer a boy. Of course Leone is no spring chicken either."

"In other words, it's time both of them were married."

Father's mind was made up. He wrote the Wexler boy. And I remember Father reading the letter to Mother. I remember it especially because he told me beforehand that he was going to read it to her.

"I'll wait until she's in a good mood," he confided in me.

"How will you be able to tell?" I asked.

"When a woman's not in a bad mood, you take a chance and assume she's in a good one."

Maybe Mother was in a good mood when Father started reading the letter, but her mood certainly changed by the time he finished.

"You know what I think?" Mother said. "I think you're just opening the door to a lot of trouble. What if Morrie Wexler doesn't like Leone? You know how that'll hurt the girl? All these years nothing has happened. Now you're building up her hopes. If nothing happens this time . . . You see the responsibility you're taking upon yourself?"

"You see it only from the woman's point of view."

"Certainly. How else would . . ."

"Perhaps Leone won't like the Wexler boy. That's a possibility, too, you know."

These terrible possibilities, however, didn't frighten Father. His eyes were clearly open to them all and yet he mailed the letter to Morrie Wexler. It told of the "wonderful girl" in Zanesville who would be a perfect match for him. It asked if he would come to our home to meet this "mature and intelligent woman."

Morrie Wexler arrived one Sunday at noon.

Sophie, Bob, Dave, and I had been awaiting his appearance with a growing excitement. We were all too young, when we had lived in Butler, to remember him.

Sophie said, "He can't be very handsome if he never got married."

"You don't have to be handsome," I corrected her, "to get married. Look at old Joe Whatchamacallit." His name was too long and Polish to pronounce, so Whatchamacallit had become our name for him. "Or even Father. He's not exactly handsome."

Still we hadn't anticipated anything like Morrie Wexler. The first thing I saw was his size—he was a mountain range turned biped. And he was fat. Then I saw his extra thick glasses and the ugliness of his face.

I whispered to Sophie, Bob, and Dave, "Leone'll take one look at him and pass out. And he'll take one look at Leone and he'll pass out."

I visualized Morrie Wexler hitting the floor in a faint, his bulk crashing right through the floor.

But nothing like that happened.

While we and Morrie Wexler were at the Sunday dinner table, Leone arrived. It was all prearranged. Mother asked Leone to stay for dinner, insisted on it. Leone said no twice and then sat down at the table.

Leone was pretty big and pretty ugly too.

I knew what Father was thinking. He was thinking, "They match."

Father liked to have things match. When he'd buy me a suit, he'd say that now I had to get a cap to match. Or when he bought furniture, which was all the time, he'd always be getting pieces to match.

Those two ugly people certainly match, I thought.

Nothing happened throughout that Sunday dinner. Leone and Morrie Wexler just sat there. They were both the quiet type. If Father hadn't been there to say, "The chicken's very tender, isn't it?" or, "Help yourself to the mashed potatoes," and things like that, nothing would have been said at all.

"Just wait till after dinner," I whispered to Bob, who was sitting next to me. "He'll ask Leone if she'll marry him."

But that didn't happen. Marriage wasn't even mentioned. Leone left. And an hour or so later Morrie Wexler said he'd have to be going if he was going to catch the evening train to Butler.

Father walked Morrie Wexler to the station.

When Father returned, Mother said, "Well, what do you think?"

Father's face was a happy smile. "Everything will be all right."

"Did he say anything to you on the way to the depot?"

"No—no— But you can't push these things. Mark my word, everything will be all right."

"Well, there's one thing sure," Mother said, "Nobody's going to say they'll make a lovely couple."

This statement of Mother's didn't make Father's face stop being happy. Why he was so confident, I didn't know. Sophie and my brothers wondered about it, too. There had been absolutely no talk of marriage, no indication that there ever would be.

"There's one thing," I told Sophie after much thought. "Leone and that fellow match. Maybe Father figures the way he does because they match."

It must have been either that or Father's intuition, for Leone and Morrie Wexler were married. In Leone's home; on a Sunday; and seven weeks from the Sunday of their meeting.

During those seven weeks, I'd heard Father say, and with great glee on each occasion, "They're corresponding. That's a good sign."

"We'll see," Mother would say.

Mother even refused to get enthusiastic after Leone and Morrie Wexler were married. She wasn't so sure the marriage would last.

"If she can make strudel the way you make strudel," Father said, "there'll be nothing to worry about."

"You know how much strudel a man that size can eat?"

Father refused to take Mother seriously. "If she can't bake enough, she'll hire an assistant. It's a perfect match. Everything will be all right."

"We'll see. I still say you take too much responsibility upon yourself when you bring two people together and marry them."

"You know," Father became suddenly very solemn, "I prayed that I'd be able to marry Leone and that boy."

I didn't forget those words of Father's. They bothered me. Could it have been Father's prayers that had turned the marital trick? Only something that partook of the miraculous nature of prayer could have been potent enough. Big, taciturn, ugly Morrie Wexler and big, taciturn, ugly Leone had to be attracted to one another. A catalyst of TNT dimensions was indicated.

I went into Father's study one day, hoping to get the answer. We got into an argument about God instead.

"Did you really pray about Leone and that Morrie Wexler getting married?" I asked Father.

"Of course."

"Did that do it? You mean if you hadn't prayed, it wouldn't have happened—they wouldn't have got married?"

Father hesitated. It was plain he wanted to be accurate. He'd told me once before that he took his talks with me seriously.

"It's a very complex situation," he said. "Many factors are involved. My prayer was one of those factors. It's impossible to say just what would have happened if I hadn't prayed that those two should get married."

"But if God wanted them to get married, He didn't need you to tell Him."

Father chuckled. "Maybe He didn't want them to, until I brought it to His attention."

"But God knows what's in your mind. You've told me that."

"Well?"

"If He knows what you're thinking, why tell Him? And anyhow He knows what you're going to think before you think, and what's going to happen before it happens. And He knows what's best. It seems to me it's an insult for just an ordinary person to tell Him."

39

FATHER AND THE ANGELS

"You don't want to pray any more, is that it?"
Father asked irritably.

It was understandable that Father suspected
the motive of my arguments concerning prayers.
I was always "forgetting" to say them. But now I
was struggling in an honest, childish way toward understanding; at the moment, there
wasn't a sacrilegious motive inside me.

Besides Father's suspecting my motives, he
didn't like to argue too much about the things in
which he believed. Too much reasoning just
"bothered your head," tainted faith, served no
worthwhile purpose.

Our argument finally reached the point where
Father said, "Why do you bother my head?"

"I just want to know," I said, "that's all."

Father became a trifle angry, angry because he
couldn't answer my questions, angry because I,
a fledgling in theology and everything else, stood
up straight and said, "I just want to know, that's
all."

"Why, you're not even born yet," Father said,
walking around his study. " 'I just want to know.'
Of course you want to know." Father, with a
gesture of his arm, indicated the books the salesman had sold him in the bookcases the salesmen had sold him. "All the learned men who
wrote those books wanted to know, too."

Father's *ad hominem* punctured my desire to
have my words defeat his words. It also dimmed

40

the momentary glow of importance I'd felt arguing with him about God and prayer.

So I left Father's study without my answer as to how that big, ugly pair had become man and wife. I despaired of ever knowing.

It became related in my mind to another riddle. The people of this riddle were the men and women of the movies. Why, I wondered, did the villains go to such arduous lengths to kiss the heroine? And why did the heroine wear herself out racing about, tipping over tables and chairs to block the path of her panting pursuer? It just didn't make sense.

I asked Mother. That was a mistake.

"You go to entirely too many movies," she said.

"Just on Sundays. That doesn't seem too much to me."

Mother shook her head. "The things they show in those moving pictures," she said. "I'll have to talk to your Father."

I overheard the conversation between Father and Mother that night. They thought I was in bed, but I was sitting on the stairway. I couldn't see them; I could just hear their voices coming from the living room.

"Must Willie go to the movies every single week?" Mother was saying.

"He's a boy."

"That's exactly what I mean. He is a boy—a very young boy."

41

"You can't keep a boy cooped up."

It went on like that for some time. Mother didn't once mention the villain-chasing-the-heroine question which had made her suddenly aware of the fact that I was seeing too many movies. Nor did Father once ask her why—really why—she was making all this fuss about the movies.

Father and Mother knew the facts of life, but they were afraid to mention them to each other. Father especially.

Throughout my childhood I was aware of this, vaguely at times, more clearly at other times. Father usually spoke frankly to me, but on this one subject he was dumb. And it bothered me that he wouldn't and couldn't tell me why the villain chased the heroine and why the heroine ran away.

One afternoon, several months after Leone and Morrie Wexler were married, Father came home early. His face was so happy Mother assumed he'd bought some more furniture.

"Well?" Mother said with weary resignation. "What is it now?"

"Music is coming into our house. Mr. Smith . . ."

"Music! Don't tell me you bought a piano!"

"Please—let me finish what I've got to say. Because I married off his daughter to Morrie Wexler, Mr. Smith is giving me a beautiful red mahogany phonograph as a present."

Father enunciated the words "beautiful red mahogany" with loving care.

Mother wasn't at all impressed. "It would have been much better," Mother said, "if Smith would have given you a check for a few dollars."

Father confided in me when Mother wasn't around. That gave me a great deal of pleasure; it made me feel as if I were a man, and a man very necessary to Father.

"You won't tell your mother or your sister or brothers?"

I shook my head.

"Mr. Smith didn't give me the phonograph —directly, that is. He said that Leone and Morrie Wexler are very happy and he thanked me and he gave me twenty-five dollars for my trouble."

"So you *bought* the phonograph!"

"I added a few cents to the twenty-five dollars. Yes, I bought it. It's a beautiful red mahogany. Just you wait till you see it."

Mr. Smith had a big furniture store out on West Main Street, but I was disappointed in the phonograph Father had selected. The whole family walked along with the furniture men as they carried the phonograph into the house.

I was disappointed because the phonograph didn't have a horn. I'd seen one in Mr. Atkinson's living room that had a horn. The horn had several American Beauty roses painted inside it. Mr. Atkinson owned the abattoir where my father slaughtered the cows, ritualistically, for the Jewish people in Zanesville. Mr. Atkinson lived next door to his slaughter house, and on several occasions when I'd gone along with Father I'd seen the rose-ornamented phonograph horn.

Father's phonograph was a cabinet-style machine. It had a name; Vitanola was its name. It didn't look like a phonograph. It just looked like a piece of furniture.

That was what Father liked about it.

Six records went with the machine. There was one by Caruso which had lyrics that were strictly Italian. "Magic Fire Spell," with the "Rustle of Spring" on the other side. One that kept singing of a place "where my caravan has rested."

I don't remember what the other three records were.

One day Bob bought a small record with a yellow label at the five-and-ten. And that was the only addition that was ever made to our record collection.

Father would often stand away from the Vitanola and look at it the way an artist looks at a painting. It was Father's way of looking at furniture.

One day I saw him putting books in the compartments where records were supposed to go.

# FOUR

Our house on Monroe Street was no castle. But Father felt that it was and so did I. Mother was always careful not to let us know how she felt.

She let Father know, however, when he had the house painted a cream yellow trimmed in chocolate.

"I don't know what's got into your head," she said.

She'd come outside and found Father and me happily watching the painters.

"What'll the members of the congregation say when they see those colors?" Mother wanted to know.

I felt sorry for Father, for I understood the position he was in. He was always telling me that as his son it was incumbent upon me to set an example. The example I had to set was as nothing compared to Father's.

"The colors are beautiful," Father said.

Mother compressed her lips and sighed. "A sensible gray would have been better."

"And I suppose a cleric black would have been best."

45

I could tell Father was disappointed that Mother didn't appreciate the cream yellow and chocolate.

Father was proud of the house on Monroe Street even before it was painted.

"It's the best in the block," he said.

This was Father's little joke, for our house was the only one in the block. The rest of the block was taken up by the West Jefferson Creamery, a warehouse filled with old brewery machinery, and a fire station. The fire station was on the corner and next door to our house.

But Monroe Street made no pretense at being exclusive. At the end of the street was the Monroe Street bridge. Toughs squatted there, busy with loafing-talk.

And in the middle of the street's length was the Monroe Street School—an old frame structure, toilets in the back, hydrant for drinking water in the yard, gaslights in only one room— the sixth grade.

The schoolhouse was the only bit of the street my sister, brothers, and I did not enjoy. Father was all for it, however. He called the school bell, a big one rung by a rope, "that blessed bell." He thought its clang beautiful because it took us off his hands.

It was on the eleventh of November, 1918, that I, for the first time, enjoyed hearing it ring. It was rung because the war was over. That time, instead of making us go to school, it released us. It also meant Father wouldn't have to go overseas as a chaplain.

When Father spoke of becoming a chaplain, Mother asked, "Have you gone crazy?"

"You think I'd look funny in a uniform. You can't imagine me riding on a horse."

"You in the army? They wouldn't take you."

I was overjoyed by this conversation. Father had always spoken against war. He said that war was a brutal, costly way of not settling anything. Nor could he interpret the Fifth Commandment to include it. I wanted Father to be for war, wanted it with an intense, almost desperate yearning. Father feeling as he did made me feel like an outsider. I wanted my father to be like the fathers of all the other children.

As soon as I reached school I made the announcement that Father was going to go into the army. There was no perhaps in my news release. Nor did I mention anything about his being a chaplain. Deep down, I was ashamed of that, too. I wanted Father to be a regular soldier, a soldier with a gun.

"He's going to ride a horse," I elaborated. "A big white one."

My imagination had seized upon Father's resemblance to Ulysses S. Grant and had him placed—with the synthesis of dreams—on Robert E. Lee's Traveller.

Rexie Reynolds, tall and in the fifth grade, grabbed me and started twisting my arm as hard as he could, his close-set blue eyes glowing.

"Your old man in the army," Rexie growled in my ear. "Yow! Little, fatty preacher in the army."

Rexie twisted my arm until pain made me sink to the ground of the school yard.

"I'll give him the good ol' Dutch rub, huh?" Rexie asked the fellows crowded around to be entertained by my writhings.

Rexie didn't wait for an answer. His knuckles dug down into my scalp in the "good ol' Dutch rub."

I cried. It wasn't the Dutch rub that hurt; Rexie's words dug down into my feelings more painfully than his knuckles working into my scalp.

That night I told Father the whole story. I needed his consolation.

"You mustn't mind too much what people say," Father said.

Father was seated, and he drew me to him so that I stood between his knees. This gesture of affection started me crying, and though I tried as hard as I could to stop, I couldn't.

Father cooed comfortingly. He brushed the hair from my forehead with his hand.

"If I hadn't told a lie," I sobbed, "it might not have happened. You said you were going to

ride a horse in the army. I said you were going
to ride a white one."

"You spoke of a white horse," Father chuckled.
"So it was a white lie. You mustn't be afraid of a
lie. A good lie can be better than bad, malicious
truthfulness. See? So don't bother your head
about this any more."

But I did bother my head about it.

I couldn't forget how wonderfully kind Father
had been to me. The only times Father ever
kissed me were on the occasions, after I had
grown up, when I left home or returned home.
It was difficult for his shy nature to display that
much overt affection. I therefore couldn't forget
how he drew me toward him, brushed the hair
from my forehead.

It was at this time that I began to think
Father wasn't just an ordinary man. He had a
more direct contact with God. He was a prophet.

I thought of him as a prophet, too, because of
a picture that was always a part of our home. It
was a picture of the Biblical prophets. The
picture was long and narrow and was hung
horizontally, usually in Father's study.

It wasn't altogether easy to think of Father as
a prophet; he was short and stout. The men of
God in the picture were gaunt and tall, physical
characteristics appropriate for the godly.

Then, too, Father was always doing things
about the house, completely foreign to the epic
grandeur of the prophets.

He enjoyed a peep into the pots on the kitchen range to find out what was being prepared for the next meal. The steam escaping from the pots made him drop the lids quickly. His peep was also speeded up by Mother.

She slapped at his hands with a playful seriousness. "You're always looking in the pots," she scolded.

"I'm hungry," he said, in just the way I might have.

"Have you finished your sermon? No. So go and finish it."

"Sermons. Sermons. You'd think people would get tired of hearing sermons, that they would reach the stage where they wouldn't need sermons."

Mother folded her arms. She could put a lot of meaning into that simple act. "Will you get out of my kitchen? Soon you'll be hearing a sermon from *me*."

Though such domestic scenes reduced Father to mere man, the fire-station episode clothed Father, unequivocally, in prophetic robes.

The Monroe Street fire station was about to be closed up permanently. Old man Deevers, one of the firemen, came next door to our house to tell Father about it.

Old man Deevers came because Father had once done him a great favor. Deevers was a man who loved the bottle as one might love an only child. The trouble came because he also loved it during working hours. For a fireman to be drunk while on duty is not a good thing. He would have been discharged if Father had not intervened.

Father told the chief of the fire department, "Let Deevers stay on and I'll assume all responsibility."

"It'll take a miracle, Reverend," the chief said. "Deevers is a black Irishman, you know that."

Father worked the miracle. He simply told Deevers that he had assumed full responsibility for fireman Deevers remaining sober. Deevers liked Father too well to do anything that would hurt him. Getting drunk would. So Deevers swallowed hard, and weaned himself away from the bad and fiery bottle.

This time it wasn't only old man Deevers who was in trouble; it was the whole Monroe Street fire station.

"They got this here new gasoline wagon up at the hose house on Hamline Avenue," Deevers explained. "So they figure they won't need our station no more. Hamline Avenue will be able to take care of any fires down this way."

"But will that one station be adequate?" Father asked.

Deevers was looking around for a place to spit. He chewed Mail Pouch. Finally, he used his handkerchief. It was blue, big as a tablecloth, and polka-dotted.

Deevers then started shaking his head. "I don't care what you say. Call me 'hind the times. But a hose house ought to have horses. Horses are more reliable than human beings—or gasoline. You take a horse . . ."

This conversation curdled to terror inside me. I wasn't thinking of the men who would be thrown out of work if the Monroe Street fire station were closed, as Father was thinking; I was thinking of losing Bill and Frank, the fire horses.

Bill and Frank were an important part of the world to me. They were beautiful—big, sorrel, fat-bellied, white stars on their noses. They seemed happy to be horses, proud to be horses.

I'd never see them any more if the station closed. Never see them race out of their stalls at eight in the morning and four in the afternoon to be hitched to the fire wagon in practice drills. Never see them go down Monroe Street for their morning exercise. Never be able to feed them sugar-corn shucks that Mother would save for me to give them.

I told Father a little of how I felt about Frank and Bill. I was ashamed to reveal the entire strength of my feeling.

Father must have understood, however. The Saturday afternoon he went to see the mayor concerning the closing of the Monroe Street fire station, he asked me if I wanted to go along.

Mother was furious. "Have you suddenly gone crazy?" she asked Father. "Taking Willie along."

My going wasn't the reason back of Mother's anger.

When we were outside, Father said to me, "She doesn't want me to see the mayor. She thinks all a rabbi has to do is pray and that's the end of it. She's really worried about me; she's afraid of what the congregation will think." Father took my hand, as we walked along. "Your mother is an extraordinary wife, did you know that?"

Extraordinary? I couldn't understand Father. All I knew was that Mother made me get up into the kitchen sink every night during the summer and wash my feet. It was because I went barefoot. I didn't like to wash my feet.

The mayor was tall and thin. Besides being the mayor, he owned a florist shop. Father and the mayor stood in the middle of the florist shop and talked about the Monroe Street fire station.

"I'm afraid there's nothing I can do," Mayor Crawford said. "If the lumberyard or the wagon-works were to say they needed the added protection of the station, that would be different."

"But what's going to happen to Deevers— he's old—to the others? Where can they get work? What can they do?"

The mayor held his lank chin, lifted his shoulders.

If it hadn't been for that statement of the mayor's about the lumberyard and the wagon-works, I would not even have thought of setting fire to Jenning's Lumberyard. It was that statement plus the picture of the prophets.

Father had told me that the prophets were men who did very important jobs for God.

The imminent danger of losing Frank and Bill, those beautiful sorrels, had a chastening effect upon me. It also made me go the limit in dramatizing my role and Father's role in the cosmic scheme of things.

Father's trying to save the fire station certainly put him in the prophet class. He was doing a job for God. Then I made the deductive leap that landed me smack into hot water.

God needed help. Father certainly needed help, helping God. I'd help Father.

By that reasoning, I appointed myself to the position of assistant prophet.

Father shook his head when we came back from our visit with Mayor Crawford. He was disheartened.

"See?" Mother said. "If you had listened to me you would have saved yourself a walk."

But Father's visit to the mayor wasn't in vain; it gave me the idea of setting fire to the lumber-yard. I'd set a blaze, I decided, which would be plenty big enough for both the Monroe Street station and the Hamline Avenue station to handle. And thus I would prove that the Monroe Street station was indispensable.

I had an awfully hard time getting the lumberyard to burn. According to the outline of my plan a really big fire was essential.

I stuffed newspaper under the piled lumber in the yard. Fear made me hurry. But at the same time it made me hesitate to put the match I'd struck to the paper.

The lumber was wet. It wouldn't make fire, but it certainly made mobile ceilings and walls of smoke.

Coughing and terrified, I ran through them and all the way home.

I managed to sneak up to my room without being seen. I practically tore my clothes off, so quickly did I get undressed. I pulled the covers over my head.

The clanging of distant fire bells went right through those covers and into my ears. And so did the shouts of people, running to the lumberyard fire.

My imagination, unfortunately, went under the covers with me. It burned innocent women and children. It fanned and spread the fire so that the greater part of Zanesville was razed. Worst of all, it had me discovered as the guilty firebug, which in turn led to Father's being discharged from his pulpit.

Facing the family at breakfast, the next morning, was a red-hot hell. I made it to the table and sat down.

"Bad fire last night, Willie," Father said.

I scattered two spoonfuls of sugar over my oatmeal, very quickly.

"What's the matter?" Father persisted. "Fires are usually a source of great pleasure to you."

"Willie!" Mother shouted.

I started, making a space of half a foot between my seat and the chair's seat. Father's questioning definitely indicated he was suspicious. Mother's shout coming on top of that certainty sounded like a policeman ordering, "Halt, fire-setter!"

"Willie!" Mother's shout went on. "Stop wolfing down your oatmeal."

I wolfed down the rest of it, and left the kitchen at a restrained run.

At school, by casual questioning, I found out what had happened at the Jenning's Lumberyard—after my speedy, coughing departure.

The Monroe Street fire station had settled the smoke over the lumberyard in record time.

"What about the Hamline hose house?" I asked quietly, hesitantly.

Frosty, so named because of a congenital red nose, whined, "They was a bust. Two blocks from the station, that new gasoline truck stops. Blooey—like that. Then they start crankin', crankin', crankin'. Everybody took turns till they was all wore out. By that time there was no more fire."

Happiness and thankfulness surged up inside me. I looked up at the sky—where God was. The fire I'd set had been a holy fire and it had served its divine purpose. Frank and Bill would not go.

During lunch hour that day, I and a half dozen other fellows went up on Hamline Avenue to look at the stalled gasoline fire wagon. Mechanics were working under it. I could not help but gloat and feel superior. I'd forgotten Father's annual sermon on pride and the fall that usually followed it. That evening I had reason to remember it.

"What's the matter you're not eating?" Mother asked me at supper that night. "You either wolf your food or you fiddle with it."

"Too much excitement," Father said, and he looked at me as though he wanted me to confirm his explanation. "That lumberyard fire last night and the excitement about it today has taken away the boy's appetite."

Shivers skimmed over my back. They accompanied my decision that Father definitely knew I had set the fire. The way he had spoken and looked at me that morning, and the way he was speaking and looking at me now proved he knew.

"Maybe a relaxing walk after supper would do us both some good," Father went on, his meaningful tone becoming progressively obvious. "A nice walk to the bridge and back."

I tried not to show any hesitancy and so I spoke a trifle too quickly, eagerly. "Sure. Sure, I'd like to go."

"Do you have to walk to the bridge?" Mother asked. "There are always bums there."

"Bums are people, too," Father said.

"Very fine people. None better."

Mother's sarcasm didn't touch Father. He liked the way the loafers at the foot of the Monroe Street bridge shouted their greetings. They seemed in turn to enjoy using the titles Rabbi or Reverend in speaking to Father. It was as though this mere verbal contact with Father added to their social stature.

"Howyuh, Revner!" (Revner seemed to be their word for Reverend.)

" 'Lo, Rabbi! Nice day."

Father would smile, lift his hand, nod his head.

Very often Father said, and with a great deal of pride, "Everybody in Zanesville knows me. Everybody."

To Father that wasn't a superficial sign of popularity; it was a sign that he had reached the people and they had accepted him.

Father and I started on our "nice walk" to the bridge.

It wasn't nice right from the start, because Father came right to the point.

"Did you do it?" Father asked—succinctly, but not cryptically.

"Do it?"

"Mr. Deevers thought he saw you at the lumberyard last night," Father went on decisively. "He wasn't sure. He was slightly intoxicated. He's been worried about the fire station's closing or he wouldn't have been intoxicated. He told me he'd gone to the lumberyard to keep out of sight and also to sleep off his intoxication."

Father never used the word drunk. In his opinion it had a gutter sound and wasn't worthy of man who was made in the image of God. Intoxicated was a much better word. There was a certain dignity to it.

Since I remained silent, Father said, "Well?"

"Old man Deevers saw me all right," I began with tentative slowness, tears fast becoming a burning film over my eyes.

Father didn't say anything. I knew it was because he didn't want to hurt me. We had stopped our walk and stood facing one another. Then I felt Father's hands on my shoulders gently asking me to trust him.

I blurted out the whole story then. My emotional state kept it from being in chronological order. Tact saw to it that I made certain omissions.

I didn't tell him anything about the prophet angle. If I had told him I thought he was a

59

prophet, I knew he would have turned red with embarrassment. And I was ashamed to say I'd considered myself an assistant prophet.

Father had once told me the secret of speaking before an audience.

"Just think of them as heads of cabbages," Father had said.

That secret formula had helped Father over his first few sermons, but it was of no value at all to me now.

"I didn't want them to close up the fire station," I managed to say. "Old man Deevers and all the other firemen would have lost their jobs. I just wanted to show that they needed the fire station. And that's what I did show."

That of course would have been Father's motivation had he set fire to Jenning's Lumberyard. It wasn't mine. Mine was primarily concerned with the two fire horses, Frank and Bill. But I thought Father could better understand a motivation that would have moved him. Though I set a fire for the sake of two beautiful horses, I didn't think Father would. Being an adult, he thought more of people.

When I'd finished my statement, Father spoke for the first time. "If you were going to do a thing like that," Father said, "you should have come to me. Spoken to me about it."

"I was going to. I thought about it. But . . ."

"But you were afraid I would have forbidden it."

"You'd have put your foot down. Sure. And then nothing would have happened."

"Will you promise me one thing?" Father asked, smiling.

"Yes."

"Always come to me. And I promise that there'll be times I won't put my foot down."

Father asked me if there were still things I was keeping from him. He wanted me to speak up about them.

The prophet angle came to mind immediately. But I couldn't make my tongue form the words that would tell my father about it.

I felt obligated to tell Father something. He deserved it, considering how understanding he'd been about what I'd done at the lumberyard.

So I told him about Freddy Yorkin's wife. Freddy the Tailor they called him. I knew how bashful and shy Father was, but I felt that I had to tell him something.

"Back in Freddy Yorkin's tailor shop is a lot of steam from the pressing machines," I said by way of introduction. "It was when I went to get your black suit that had been cleaned and pressed."

"I noticed the coat sleeve was soiled," Father said. "You dropped it, did you?"

I shook my head. I didn't want to go on with this story about Freddy Yorkin's wife that I'd kept secretly to myself. But I felt myself being carried on the momentum of the words with which I'd started the story.

"No. It's not about your suit. Mrs. Yorkin was back there. She was naked. This is one of the things I haven't told you and I've always thought I should have told you."

"Willie!"

Father looked scared. He was rubbing his hand around in his beard.

"Mrs. Yorkin," I was on the last dip of the roller coaster now, "she was taking a steam bath back there."

Father looked relieved. It was plain he'd expected something much worse. I was sorry I'd disappointed him.

"But she was all naked," I said.

# FIVE

To make Father laugh out loud during the Friday evening services seemed like a great idea. Dave was younger than I, but not less adventurous. So we plotted.

Father didn't face the members of his congregation when he conducted services in the synagogue. Throughout the earlier part of my childhood, I thought it was because he was facing God. It seemed very logical that Father should face God, since he was praying to Him and not to the people.

At one point in the Friday services, however, Father would turn around. Not to face the people, but to face the front door. As he turned, faced the door, and then turned back again, Father sang.

The song was in Hebrew, but I knew what it meant. Father had told me. The Sabbath was thought of as a bride—poetically, of course—and Father's song was a song of welcome. That was why Father turned and faced the door.

Dave, the other kids, and I always sat in the

63

last pew; it made conversation during the service possible.

"Do you come to pray or do you come to talk?" Father often asked me. He didn't want an answer. He merely wanted a reasonable amount of decorum out of me from then on.

We not only sat in the last pew and talked, but we pinched one another, tickled one another, and fought. We tried, as best we could, to have all this fun as silently as possible, so we could continue it as long as possible. We weren't always successful.

I didn't mind when Mr. Hyman, the short, white-bearded beadle, came over to the last pew and turned a stream of scalding Yiddish on us. *"Shtill!"* He kept hissing that word at us. *"Shtill!"* It was pleasurable disturbing an adult, even old Mr. Hyman.

Dave and I discovered that it was also fun to wave to Father when he turned around to welcome the Sabbath. Father couldn't help but smile when we waved. We saw how hard he had to struggle to keep from laughing out loud, and that observation gave Dave his idea.

"Next Friday night," Dave said, "instead of waving let's do something that'll really make him laugh, make him really bust out laughing."

"You want to get him in trouble with the congregation?" I asked.

Tuesday of the following week Dave said to me, "You know what I'm going to do?"

I didn't know what he was talking about. "You get any fatter and you'll pop the seat of your pants, that's what you'll do," I said. Dave had a healthy chubbiness, but by any boy's high athletic standards he was simply fat.

Dave wouldn't tell me what he was going to do. I'd hurt his feelings. To be without a brain was better, according to our youthful values, than to be fat.

When Friday night came, I'd forgotten that Dave planned to make Father laugh out loud in front of all the people in the synagogue. But Dave hadn't forgotten.

Dave was sitting at the end of the pew near the center aisle. The last pew, of course.

Father turned slowly to greet the Sabbath. He turned with dignity. He sang beautifully. I liked his singing better than Caruso's—better than the one Caruso record we had at home.

Father was short, but he actually seemed tall when he sang. It was because Father became a part of his singing, and singing always seemed tall to me, never short. Besides, Father wore his black velvet skull cap in the synagogue. It was six inches high and seemed a part of Father when he sang.

My thoughts lifted and there was Dave in the aisle, and turned so that he faced the door. He was bowing at the waist, his right arm across his belt, his left out to the side. It was a welcoming bow. Only the invisible Sabbath came through the door at the front of the synagogue.

"Come, my beloved, to meet the bride," Father sang in Hebrew. "Let us welcome . . ."

The congregation couldn't see what Dave was doing; they sat in the front pews and faced Father. But they would hear Father if he bust out laughing. And Father might really bust out laughing because Dave was bowing to the Sabbath.

That frightening possibility struck me with the suddenness of a slap.

I reached into the aisle to grab Dave.

I didn't get my fingers to Dave's coattail, for I saw a smile on Father's face. It was a smile of pleasure; it, plainly, was not the kind that would tumble out of control and into laughter.

Father's smile said, "I'm very proud of you, David, my son. I'm very happy that you bowed the way you did. Very happy, indeed!"

Had Father suddenly gone mad?

Dave didn't see Father's smile because he was too busy bowing. The moment Father said the blessing over the wine, at the end of the service, Dave scooted out of the synagogue.

"By the time he gets home," Dave told me just before he hurried away, "he won't remember what I did anymore. Anyhow, he didn't bust out laughing. Why should he be sore?"

But Father didn't forget the bowing episode. I didn't expect him to. That Dave was going to get it from Father was what I was looking forward to and expecting.

All the way home I wondered about Father's smile. He might have said something to me immediately about Dave and his little bowing trick, if it hadn't been for Mr. Berman—the treasurer of the congregation.

Mr. Berman lived on Kelly Street. He always walked home with Father after services, since Kelly Street was on our way.

Mr. Berman walked with his hands behind his back, under his coat. He was big and fat and waddled.

"Wheat," Mr. Berman said. "Wheat is what's affecting the world markets. The price of wheat." He stuck out his lower lip and wagged his head as he spoke—authoritatively. "You take the winter wheat in Yugoslavia . . ."

Father nodded his head, an is-that-so nod. Father didn't pretend to know anything about wheat as it affected world markets. That nod of Father's flattered Mr. Berman, pleased him. I could tell Father knew that it did too. But I couldn't tell if Father was thinking about punishing Dave for bowing in the synagogue, at the same time that he was nodding to Mr. Berman.

I and the other kids who were with me that night quacked like ducks, synchronizing our quacking to Mr. Berman's waddle. We made sure, however, that we were far enough behind

Father and Mr. Berman so that they would not hear.

Mr. Berman always talked about wheat, or a two-thirds vote of the Senate, or labor-is-no-good. I wondered why he didn't talk more about his junkyard. It was situated behind his home and was very impressive. The metal was piled so high that when you stood at the foot of it, the rusty, rounded top of the pile touched the blue of the sky. I guess I stood looking up at that metal hill touching the sky as often as Mr. Berman talked to Father about wheat, the Senate, and labor.

I could hardly wait till Father would give it to Dave. But Father waited patiently until after supper before he spoke to Dave. He was sure Mother was in the kitchen, too. Mother, Father knew, had a way of making simple matters seem complicated.

"You shouldn't have done what you did tonight," Father said.

Dave said, "Aw," quickly, as though he had been holding that expletive in readiness.

"You don't understand," Father said, his voice quiet and mild. "I'm really not displeased." He shook his head and smiled.

Dave stopped squirming; his pained face relaxed; he stared at Father. I wasn't surprised the way Dave was. I suppose it was because I'd known Father longer than Dave, being older than Dave.

"You must understand, David, that there are certain advantages in having a set ritual."

Neither Dave nor I knew what Father was talking about. We had even less of a conception of what he would be saying next.

He went on to state that long usage made for the traditions of a religion. The Sabbath had been greeted for a very long time in just the way Father greeted it. Worshipers were familiar with that greeting and had grown to love it. What you know well—thoroughly—you love, can only love.

"So you see," Father concluded, looking at Dave, "the people couldn't possibly accept your innovation. Bowing to the Sabbath is a new greeting and therefore strange."

Gosh, I thought, can it possibly be that Father doesn't understand that Dave was just trying to make him bust out laughing? Can it possibly be that he doesn't know Dave should be punished?

I was wondering this all the time Father was talking.

Father stealthily attracted my attention. He was smiling, and he blinked his eyes at me several times. Father couldn't wink. It was strange, but he couldn't close one eye without the other one closing, too. So instead of winking, Father would blink his eyes. Father was careful that Dave didn't see the blinking.

I was disappointed. All along I'd been looking

forward to seeing Dave get it good and plenty, for trying to make Father bust out laughing in the synagogue. I was disappointed in Father too.

The way Father handled Dave that night was typical of the way Father handled his family— and all Zanesville, for that matter.

"If a harmless method can produce a very good result, what's wrong with it?" Father often asked.

It was always before Mother that Father posed this question; Mother always advocated a less subtle approach to the problems of life.

There was the time, for example, when I got into a fight—a skin-off-the-nose, to-a-finish fight —in the alley back of our house. Mother used a broom on me, Father a few very calmly and carefully chosen sentences. They turned out to be worse than the broom. Because of them, I'd never be able to get into a fight anymore.

Fred Fulton—Steamboat was what the kids called him—was my opponent in the fight. He was bigger and older than I. As sadistic as a boy can be too.

If I had been a grasshopper, he'd have yanked out my legs and wings. Since I wasn't a grasshopper, Steamboat had to be satisfied with sneaking up behind me and yanking out my shirttail. And often he'd take my cap away.

"I'm going to throw this old cap up on a chimney," he always threatened.

To Steamboat, a chimney was obviously the direst and most inaccessible place to throw some-one's cap.

I thought of going to Father for advice. But then I'd be a tattletale. Better to suffer than to be a tattletale.

Besides, I wasn't sure Father would under-stand. He didn't, for example, understand how much muscles could mean to a fellow.

One day Father opened the bathroom door while I was looking at my biceps, estimating their growth, hoping that they had grown, feeling their hardness, and the pride that hardness en-gendered.

"What are you doing?" Father asked.

I was startled out of my preoccupation. "Do-ing?" I said. "Nothing."

"I need to use the bathroom. You can do noth-ing outside. What I have to do, I must do in-side."

But Father knew what I was doing, and he must have thought a lot about it.

That afternoon when I came home from school, he called me into his study.

"I've noticed that you take a great deal of in-terest in bodily strength," Father said to me.

"Oh, not such an awfully great deal."

"I suppose it's only natural for a boy." Thoughtfully, Father scratched his cheek where there wasn't any beard. "Still I don't want you to feel that all growing up amounts to is getting a stronger right arm."

At school the next day, I figured out a good answer for Father. One he could appreciate. I knew it wouldn't be long before I'd be able to use it.

"But the body's the temple of the soul, isn't it?" I asked Father when the question of muscles came up again.

Father had once in a sermon said the body was the temple of the soul, when he told the congregation not to eat pills in the same manner and quantity as they might eat gum drops. He used it in another sermon directed especially to Mr. Samuels who worked too hard and ruined his bodily health. Then there was the sermon for Edith Lippman who was running around late at night and making her father and mother worry because of it.

I knew for whom Father intended some of his sermons, because he'd sometimes tell Mother and I'd hear. I often wondered if those for whom they were intended always knew.

"The body *is* the temple of the soul," Father said, and he seemed proud that I had learned that important fact. "But a temple can be simple and yet beautiful and strong. If your body bulges with muscles, it will be like a temple that's elaborate and garish."

I was stumped. I thought I had Father stumped, but I was stumped. Mother told me

quite frequently, "Your father has a fine mind."
I guessed that that was why Father smiled, but
didn't laugh, when Dave bowed in the synagogue.
And why Father always had an answer. If it came
to the worst, he'd say, "Don't bother my head."
That, I felt, was an answer, too.

And I guess it was because Father didn't understand just how I felt about muscles that I
didn't go to him about the problem of Fred
Steamboat Fulton.

Steamboat's taking my cap for the fiftieth
time set off our fight. He threatened to throw
it up on a chimney. When I tried to snatch it
from him, he held it high beyond my reach. Or
he put it behind his back and tortured me by
switching it from hand to hand as I tried to get
it away from him.

I wanted my cap. For some preadolescent reason, it seemed very valuable to me and, once
lost, irreplaceable. One's cap was equal to the
whole world.

"Give it to me!" Tears of rage and anxiety
burned my eyes. "You give it to me! Give it to
me! Give it to me!"

"I'm going to throw it up on a chimney."
Steamboat made the gesture of tossing it away
from him, high into the air. "Here she goes.
Here she . . ."

Unfortunately for Steamboat, his gesture left
his entire left flank completely exposed. I swung.

My right fist landed. Steamboat grounded on the cinders of the alley. And so did his courage.

He fought, but he was no match for my righteous fury. Soon his nose was bleeding. I yanked his shirttail out for all the countless time he had yanked mine out. I ripped his shirt. How could ripping a shirt fill one with such tingling, wild delight?

An audience soon made an amphitheatre around Steamboat, me, and our fight. Old man Deevers and some of the other firemen were among those present.

I fought silently on. Steamboat had had enough, but I hadn't enough of giving him enough. Then Mother arrived—and with a broom.

"You go right home!" Mother ordered and she took swipes at me with the broom. "Now! This instant! You ought to be ashamed!"

I dodged the broom and Mother. And I maneuvered so that I could get in a poke at Steamboat occasionally.

The crowd in the alley enjoyed this more than they had my fight with Steamboat. They laughed and shouted advice to Mother.

"You ought to be ashamed!" Mother scolded every time she swung the broom at me.

But I wasn't ashamed.

Mother managed to chase me a few yards from Steamboat, but I dodged and got back at Steamboat. One punch. Another. And I was away again.

Some wag in the audience shouted, "Steamboat's sprung a leak!"

Steamboat was crying.

"You crybaby you," I spat at Steamboat.

I didn't have to hit Steamboat after that. Those three words of utter contempt were my *coup de grâce*.

Mother made me go up to my bedroom without supper that night. I didn't care. I lay on the bed and looked at the ceiling and didn't care. Beating Steamboat as I had done made me feel powerful and brave. He had been able to bully me because I had been afraid of him. The ceiling over me became a screen for my imagination. I saw myself fighting with kids who were even bigger than Steamboat. They were all powerless before my heroic strength. I was wonderful.

Downstairs Mother was talking to Father. She didn't think me wonderful.

"He must take after your side of the family," I heard Mother say. "He certainly doesn't take after mine."

That was a favorite refrain of Mother's. Her simple genetics, born of exasperation.

"But there was some excuse," Father said in my defense. "This older boy tormented Willie."

I left their conversation and was taking an imaginary gun from an imaginary youthful

75

giant with whom I was fighting, when I heard footsteps coming up the stairs. Father? I sat up. Father came through the door and to my bed. I couldn't forget how he had handled the bowing episode in the synagogue. I tensed myself to be ready for anything.

"You feel all right?" Father asked.

"Sure."

"He didn't hurt you at all, Willie?"

"Naw."

"I can see your face is scratched. There's some skin off your nose."

I was thinking that Father had just called me Willie. I'd told him to call me Bill, told him a trillion times, but he always called me Willie. Willie! He might as well call me Mary or Susie. He might as well.

"You think it was worth it?" Father asked. "Fighting and getting your nose scratched. Upsetting your mother the way you have. Besides, people look up to you. If you, the son of a rabbi, fight, how can I expect the other children in the community to behave differently?"

"Well, he was always pushing me around," I protested. "I'm not going to let anyone push me."

"You should have come to me. That would have been the brave thing to do."

Brave to tattle? Then I remembered what a funny conception of bravery Father had.

Father thought Jones the barber was a brave man.

Father always got his haircuts on Friday for the honor of the Sabbath. He came home from the barbershop one Friday and told Mother, "You know, that Mr. Jones the barber is a brave man."

After that, every time I had my hair cut I tried by staring at Jones to see some aspect of his bravery. I couldn't.

Jones the barber was just an ordinary bald-headed man; where he wasn't bald he was gray. His stomach always made gurgling digestive noises. He stood very close when he was cutting my hair, and I enjoyed listening to the infinite variations of those noises. Sometimes I heard a string of penny firecrackers go off inside his stomach.

What else was there about Jones? He wore thick glasses. He'd always be turning away from the barber chair and my haircut to cough. He smiled a great deal too. But I couldn't see anything at all brave about him.

Mr. Jones' home was divided by his barbershop. His home had been built on each side of the shop as additions. Consequently, Mrs. Jones would always be crossing the barbershop when she went from a room in one addition to a room in the other addition. She had big, solid arms—smooth as soapstone—with dimples at the elbows. Those dimples interested me almost as much as her husband's gurgling stomach. But naturally they had nothing to do with Mr. Jones' being a brave man.

Why, once, Father had even said that all men and women were brave.

It was obvious Father knew little about bravery.

And there was another reason why I didn't go to Father about Steamboat. I couldn't imagine Father had ever been a boy. He said he had and I knew he had, but just the same I could never believe it.

He told me that when he was a child in London, he once had a fight with another boy.

"I revolved my fists around one another," Father said, "and I did it so fast that the boy became frightened and ran away."

And as he told me the story, he took what was a fighting stance for him and revolved his fists around one another like speeding armatures to show me just what he had done.

There were other things that let me know, though I wouldn't be convinced, that Father had been a boy and that he had spent his boyhood in England.

Letters from his sisters in London—my aunts —came to us. Your sister Leah, your sister Rosie, they were signed. Were they genuine sisters? I had never seen them. They were just pictures and letters—to me. Nebulous and unreal as the time when I would be grown up, with money in my pants pockets, to jingle.

And Father often told me of the hot peas children would buy from vendors on London streets.

And there were idioms in his speech that were English and unfailingly strange to my brothers, sister, and me.

Father would say "By the bye," when he meant incidentally.

And when he'd leave a group of people, he'd say, "Goodbye all."

Still I couldn't imagine Father—stout and with a beard and more than twice as old as me—as a boy. So, even though he claimed to have been in a fight once himself, how could he understand my fight with Steamboat?

"You come to me the next time," Father was saying. "Don't start beating boys up before you've come to me. Now go down and have your supper. And I'd better put some carbole water on your nose."

Father used diluted carbolic acid as an antiseptic when he did a circumcision. Because it was diluted, he called it carbole water.

After supper, I fell asleep with my head resting on the round dining-room table. Father draped me over his shoulder and carried me up to bed.

"I suppose I'll have to be doing this," he grunted to Mother under the weight of his load, "until the day he's married."

Through the haze of sleep, I thought Father meant that when I was married my wife would inherit the job of carrying me to bed. I imagined Mother carrying Father. It made a funny picture, for Father was fat and Mother wasn't. Maybe all wives didn't carry their husbands to bed. But if some didn't, then maybe mine wouldn't. So Father was mistaken in figuring that he would no longer have to carry me to bed once I was married. . . .

I awakened while Father was undressing me. "I can undress," I said, sleepily. "Go 'way. I'm not a baby."

"All right," Father said. "All right. I'm thankful you're no longer a baby."

Still he stopped at the head of the stairs and asked me if I was feeling all right. He was still thinking about my fight with Steamboat. And I was thinking, with anguish, that I'd not be able to have a fight again as long as I lived. Not if I had to go to Father first—like he'd told me to do. I felt trapped.

"Sure I'm all right," I whined. "What's a little fight? You talk like I'm a baby."

"You think it's so bad being a baby? Some day you won't think so." He went down a couple steps, stopped. "Being a baby is as fine as being an apple on a tree. Good night. Sleep tight."

Father had no sooner gone downstairs than Mother came up.

Father didn't kiss me or hug me, because he was too shy for that sort of an emotional display. Mother didn't do it often either. She was always too busy sweeping, cooking, sewing, and telling Father and her children to behave.

But Mother held me tight to her now. I was standing there in my underwear when she'd swooped me to her. I didn't know why, but I supposed it had some connection with my having been in a fight with Steamboat. That afternoon she'd tried to hit me with a broom, and now she was acting this way. She was funny. And Father had had to go and use his fine mind on me. I'd rather he'd used a broom.

A hot tear hit my collarbone. It came from Mother. My collarbone wasn't covered by my underwear.

Mother held me tighter still. She was flat—all the way down. She was like the ironing board, I thought, that I had to carry up from the cellar every Tuesday morning.

## SIX

SUNDAY at the dinner table Mother wanted to know if I had gone completely crazy.

"Don't get excited," Father said.

"He says he won't eat," Mother reminded Father frantically. "Didn't you hear him?"

"He'll eat. He'll eat."

"I didn't say I wouldn't eat," I said, correcting both my father and mother. "I said I wouldn't eat that meat. That I'd never eat any meat. Not if I live to be a trillion years old."

I tried to keep my voice from trembling. The great men in all ages were persecuted, Father had said so in more than one sermon; that was the reward in store for all those who were ahead of their time. Though I were stoned, I told myself, I had to be brave, brave as William S. Hart.

"And if you don't eat meat," Mother said, cutting furiously at the veal cutlet on her plate, "what will you eat?"

"There are plenty of things besides meat."

Mother let her knife and fork drop to the table. "But from where will you get your strength?" The words caught in Mother's throat;

82

her mind must have been flashing a picture of her son, emaciated and in a wheel chair. "From where?"

Father shook his head at Mother, to quiet her. He leaned toward me, smiling. Sophie was seated between Father and me at the table.

"Why, suddenly," he laughed a little, "do you have something against a very delicious veal cutlet?" He looked at Sophie, who was gnawing on the bone of her cutlet, as proof that the cutlet was delicious.

I folded my arms. "I don't want to eat anything that lived and walked around. If you want to know."

"He's gone crazy," Mother said.

Sophie giggled.

Bob went right on eating. So did Dave. This wasn't the first time something had happened at the dinner table.

As for Father, he just looked at me and scratched his cheek, just above the line his beard made.

Mother must have decided on shock to dissipate my insanity, for she picked up her fork, pointed it at my plate, and ordered, "Eat!"

"See what you've done to your mother," Father said softly, entreatingly. "How you've upset her."

My folded arms tightened. "Well, I'm not going to eat any dead meat." Finality—absolute, irrevocable—was in my declaration.

Sophie put the gnawed bone down, giggling.

83

"You silly," she said. "How can you eat meat if it isn't dead? You want to eat live meat?"

Sophie was close enough for me to pull her hair. That was my first impulse. William S. Hart was stalking about in my subconscious, however, and William S. Hart would not have pulled Sophie's hair.

I stood up, stiff, grim. I looked around the circle of the dining-room table. They didn't understand me. Genuine hurt stabbed at me through the dramatic role I was playing—even Father didn't understand me. I turned and walked from the table.

"He hasn't eaten anything!" I heard Mother exclaim. "He should at least have some corn flakes! A *fine kuchen!* Something!"

I'll waste away, I thought. I'll lose all my strength. I'll die. I'll show all of them.

And there behind me were Sophie's sadistic giggles, Bob and Dave agreeing that Father and Mother let me go till I get good and hungry, Mother shouting that I come back and eat corn flakes.

We were living on Adair Avenue, in a section of Zanesville called the Terrace, when this happened. Behind our back porch was a steep unpaved hill, a sort of alley. November had made the ground hard, had filled the sky with sad gray clouds.

As I went down the hill, I told myself that spiritually I was utterly alone in the world.

"Willie . . . Willie . . . !"

I turned and there was Father trying to come down the steep hill. Father had never come down that hill behind our house before. Because he was too fat. Because it was too steep.

He was about halfway down, coming down sidewise. I hurried up to him and took his arm and held it as though it and Father were fragile china.

Try as I did to tell Father that he ought to go back up the hill, he insisted on continuing his descent. So I held to his arm, and he took one slow sidewise step at a time and, finally, we were at the bottom of the hill. By that time, I no longer felt that I was a lone figure walking about in an unfriendly world.

Later on, when I thought about it, I decided Father hadn't come down the hill just to be coming down the hill. Then a month later when Father had something in a sermon about Life being a hill, and about getting to know people on the hill of Life, I knew definitely why he had had me help him down the hill.

Father and I walked down Linden Avenue together.

We kept walking, walking. Father didn't say anything. I didn't either. The quiet didn't stay the same; it seemed to get quieter and quieter. Too quiet.

"Well, if you think you're going to get me to eat meat," I said. "You're not."

Father smiled. It was like the smile of a mother rocking a baby in her arms.

"I can see by your smile you think you're going to persuade me," I said.

Father shook his head. "I'm just eager to understand you, Willie."

All I knew was that whenever we took walks, Father came out ahead. It was Father's fine mind, of course. It occurred to me that perhaps if I didn't hold back anything, but was perfectly frank, I might defeat him.

Father started off by saying that according to the Bible, animals were made for man.

I couldn't say the Bible was wrong. My oldest brother Sy might be able to, but I couldn't.

"But it doesn't say you have to eat meat," I said instead. "Like Mother pointing a fork at my plate, shouting that I eat. It doesn't say there is anything wrong in not eating meat if you don't want to."

"But as Mother says, you may lose your strength."

"An elephant doesn't eat meat. And elephants aren't exactly weak."

"But you're not an elephant. Are you, Willie?"

"Of course I'm not. But just the . . ."

"You don't want to be cruel to animals. That's what's in your mind, isn't it?"

I couldn't tell Father all the things that were in my mind. Father was easy to talk to, but there were some thoughts—the terrible ones and

the very beautiful ones—you just couldn't tell
anybody. I knew Father wouldn't laugh if I told
him, like a lot of people would. I didn't know
exactly why I couldn't tell him—but I couldn't.

I couldn't tell him about the rabbits, red
bloody slits down their lengths, hanging in front
of the store next to the Schultz Opera House.
They'd made me decide never to eat meat again.
I'd seen them yesterday after I came out of the
show. There were pumpkins out in front of the
store. Bushels of ears of popcorn. And on long,
sharp, iron hooks, the rabbits hanging there dead
and bloody.

"It's just—it's just that I don't want to eat
anything that's alive—that once was alive, I
mean." Those poor rabbits were hanging, stiff,
bloody, right in my mind. "Never! Never! I'm
never going to eat meat!"

"Shhh. Don't be so excited. Straighten your
cap, Willie. Here comes Mr. Myerson."

I straightened my cap for Father and Mr.
Myerson.

Father and Mr. Myerson stopped and talked.
Father talked. Mr. Myerson hardly ever said
anything.

"You know why he's so quiet," Mother once
told Father. "When he was a bit of a child someone laughed at something he said. That's why
now he's quiet as a mouse in a trap."

Mr. Myerson had a wonderful scenic nose.
It was bumpy and red and purple. I enjoyed

looking at it, while Father talked to Mr. Myerson.

"Good," Father was saying to Mr. Myerson. "Come for supper tonight. And beginning tomorrow, you can have dinner with us every day."

Mr. Myerson smiled and nodded his head. He said goodbye, not by saying goodbye, but by lifting his hand, bowing and walking away from us.

I felt turgid with happiness at the thought of Mr. Myerson eating at our house. Bob, Dave, and Sophie were happily excited, too.

Long before supper, I stood on the front porch with my brothers and sister. Each of us wanted to be the first to catch a glimpse of Mr. Myerson.

"We'll be able to see him a mile away," I said. "Because of his nose."

After a while, Mother made us all go into the house.

"You want to freeze?" she scolded. "This is November, not June. He'll come. He'll come. When your father arranges something, it's arranged." And then Mother addressed me specifically. "So what do you think you're accomplishing by not eating meat? You see, your portion is going to be eaten by Mr. Myerson."

"Is that why he asked Mr. Myerson?"

"What do you think?"

I stared at Mother, but I was thinking of Father's treachery.

Father was trimming his beard with the scissors when I found him. Father could use scissors, but he wasn't allowed to use a razor. The bathroom door was open, and he was bent forward, his face close to the mirror. His shirt was off and his suspenders were hanging down over his trousers.

Father turned his face from the mirror and asked me what I wanted. I told him.

"But I couldn't see the meat go to waste," Father said imploringly.

Father received three pounds of meat daily from Johnny Riker, the butcher. Free—no charge at all. There were two meat blocks in the butcher shop. One was for kosher meat; the other for non-kosher. Every morning—for the two hours, during which the kosher meat was sold—Father was in the butcher shop. He saw to it that no meat passed from one block to the other. I liked to think of Father as a guard, the meat as contraband, the two blocks as two adjacent countries. Father also had another duty in the butcher shop, he cut certain veins out of the kosher meat, as prescribed by Jewish law.

I knew this, and I knew it was completely against Father's nature to waste any of the three pounds of meat he received for these services of his in the butcher shop. Father was always vividly aware of all the needy people in the world. Consequently, it hurt him to waste anything.

Mr. Myerson was a bookkeeper. Maybe book-keepers were poor. "Is Mr. Myerson a needy man?" I asked Father.

"He doesn't have anyone here in Zanesville. He's adrift. A bachelor. And I assure you he's in need of one of your mother's meals every day. That makes him a needy man—don't you think?"

"I suppose so," I said.

I wasn't completely certain, for I always thought of the needy as children who looked like skeletons and were dressed in dirty scraps. The children on the letterheads of the letters Father received whenever there was a relief drive.

Father put the scissors down and started getting into his shirt. "Willie," he said. "Now—I —I respect your feelings and intentions in all this, but there's this that occurs to me. Your respect for life doesn't take into consideration the fact that plants are alive too."

"But it's not the same!"

"A carrot, a plant of any kind, is alive."

"But a carrot doesn't walk. You—you know what I mean. A cow"—I was thinking of rabbits not cows, not rabbits hopping across fields, but rabbits on hooks—"a cow is more like a person."

"But doesn't it fulfill a worth-while purpose by being food for man? Out of its flesh, as it were, comes the music and literature and all the no-bility of man."

"But what if there are some cows that don't want that? Anyhow, none of them know what you just said. It's not fair to them. You didn't ask them. So it's just not fair."

"All right," Father said, buttoning his coat and starting down the stairs. "All right."

"You're thinking of that three pounds of meat." I was close behind Father. "You're afraid you might think I'm right and you don't want to give it up. That's why you say all right. You know I'm right and you don't want to listen to me."

Father turned around so quickly on the stairs, I bumped into him. "Whatever you do, Willie, don't bother my head now. Mr. Myerson will soon be here."

I didn't say another word. Victory was warm and pleasant inside me. Father didn't want to argue because he felt—really felt—that I was right.

And Mr. Myerson—of course I didn't know that then—was to add to my victory and to Father's defeat.

Mr. Myerson did not come alone. He came with a cello, his arm around it. He was like a little man with his arm around a fat woman.

"Just to play before eating," he explained.

"That was very thoughtful of you," Father said. "Very few people have the luxury of having music before their meals."

Sophie stepped forward eagerly. "What piece

you going to play?" she asked. "What piece? Huh?"

Reticent Mr. Myerson smiled at Sophie and nodded his head. His smile and wordlessness scared Sophie. She backed up quickly and stepped—almost darted—behind Bob.

We ate in the dining room, instead of in the kitchen, in honor of Mr. Myerson.

But before we went into the dining room, from the library, Mr. Myerson played on his cello. Mother didn't hear him; she stayed in the kitchen, having told Father she had too much to do to listen to screechings. Screechings was the word she was always to use in regard to Mr. Myerson's playing.

Like Mother, I didn't hear Mr. Myerson's music. I was too busy looking at Mr. Myerson's bumpy red nose—that Mother said had come out of a bottle—the movement of his arm as he played, and studying the shine and contours of his wonderful cello.

Mother came in carrying a steaming, heaping serving dish between her two hands and announced that supper was ready by saying, "The supper will get cold!"

Mother had no respect for Mr. Myerson's music—not, at least, when it made one's supper cold.

Mr. Myerson stopped playing in midbar. We all watched him as he stood the cello up in the corner, carefully.

"That was fine," Father told Mr. Myerson as he came to the table. "Very fine."

Mr. Myerson smiled.

Mother said, "Would you like to have nice, brown, breaded veal cutlets, Mr. Myerson? We had them at noontime, for dinner. So we're not having them now."

Mr. Myerson shook his head. "No," he said.

"You don't like veal?" Mother asked.

"It's the stomach." Mr. Myerson patted his stomach, and the expression he twisted upon his face suggested nausea. "The stomach."

"Veal won't hurt you," Mother said. "Veal is light."

"I play the cello, for the stomach," Mr. Myerson answered. "A little before I eat." He nodded his head. "A little after I eat." He nodded his head again, a nod for the rhythm of each of the sentences. "For the stomach it's good, the music."

I'd never heard Mr. Myerson utter so many consecutive words. I felt sorry for him. I didn't feel sorry for Mother who was determined to serve Mr. Myerson the veal cutlets I had refused to eat for dinner.

I wanted to help Mr. Myerson express himself. "Maybe he doesn't eat meat," I said.

"Yes, yes," Mr. Myerson said, eagerly. And there was that smile of his that had frightened Sophie.

"You're a vegetarian!"

As I recall, both Father and Mother made that startled, incredulous exclamation in unison. Father was startled; Mother, incredulous. The problem of not wasting any of his daily allotment of meat jumped up in front of Father again. And Mother couldn't believe that a grown man could be so foolish as even to try to live without the strengthening properties of meat.

"Sure he's a vegetarian," I said, jumping up joyously.

"Willie!" Mother scolded. "Sit down."

I sat down.

"Well," Father said musingly, and with the grace of a sportsman in defeat, "if Mr. Myerson's stomach doesn't permit him to eat meat, we'll just have to find good wholesome things for him that he can eat."

So in spite of the fact that Mr. Myerson wouldn't eat some of Father's free meat, he stayed on with us as a boarder.

But Father wasn't at all discouraged by Mr. Myerson's having turned out to be a vegetarian. He knew there were still plenty of people in the world who ate meat. And he started looking for them—almost at once.

Father brought up the subject of a new boarder one Saturday just as we were finishing dinner—after he had told Mother how wonderful the chicken soup had been, how sweet and tasty her chicken. As for her strudel, Father had to resort to Yiddish to fully express himself. You

went to the bottom of her memory for almost forgotten delicacies her mother had prepared for her when she was a child.

There was *nahet,* chick peas prepared with rice and honey. *Mamaliga,* corn meal mush, topped with butter and cottage cheese. *Schwartz-ah Taevil,* egg plant chopped up with onions and an unbelievably great quantity of oil. Green peppers—and there was a name for this dish, too, which I have forgotten—stuffed with farina and nuts and vegetables.

Mother wouldn't let everyone eat these dishes. They were only for me. She was afraid Bob, Dave, or Sophie, if they had just one delicious taste, might stop eating meat.

"One crazy person in the family is enough," she said.

"Don't say Willie is crazy," Father said. "The great of every age have been termed crazy by those who didn't understand them."

"And Willie's the great of every age?" Mother asked, slightly impatient with Father.

I felt that Father could afford to take my side now, with Mr. Josephs eating my daily portion of meat. He still didn't understand me. But Father was to prove me wrong—as usual.

One evening, Mr. Josephs brought Mother a dog as a gift. It was a statue, made of chalk. There was an Italian who was going around our town selling them. They were used for door stops. When they were broken, you could use the pieces for writing on the sidewalks or on buildings. The nostrils of this dog were painted such a bright red it looked as if the dog had a nosebleed. And the end of its black tail became white—and a little shorter—because Dave had something he wanted to write on a sidewalk or on a building. You could write with the dog, or any part of it, because it was all chalk.

We called the dog Mr. Josephs brought, "the dog"—nothing else, just "the dog." It wasn't really a dog, we realized, and therefore shouldn't have a name.

Mother spoke of it as "that dog."

"Did I need that dog?" she asked rhetorically. "Don't I have enough dusting?"

"Well, anyhow," Father put in, lights as merry as candlelight in his eyes, "it's quiet. It doesn't bark too much."

"And it doesn't bite," I added, helping Father's joke along.

Mother, surprisingly, was in a joking mood, too. "Willie," she said, "you should talk to your brother. Scold him for hurting that dog, breaking off part of his tail."

It was this remark of Mother's—spoken innocently, unaware of consequences—that made a missionary of me and caused a lot of trouble. I forthwith set out to conquer Dave.

It was hard talking to Dave. He was playing catch with Bob in the back alley. Bob was catching and Dave was pitching. Dave would wind up and burn them in. At that moment Dave was pretending—I could tell by just the way he'd wind up and burn them in—that he was someone like Tris Speaker.

Just the same, I asked him how he would like it if he just happened to be born a cow and people got hold of him and killed him and ate him up. It was really a form of reasoning or evaluation I had learned from Father; when I did something wrong, Father would start giving me a talking to by saying, "How would you like it if . . . ?"

Dave stopped a windup and looked at me. "You crazy?" he asked. "Good and crazy? What's the use of supposin' I was born a cow?"

"But you might have been. Just as you might have been born a girl instead of a boy."

Dave wound up quickly and burned the ball in.

It was such a swift one that Bob jumped aside, howling in protest. The ball went down the hill.

Bob started after the ball. "The next time you do that," he shouted, "you're chasin' it!"

"If you're a punk catcher," Dave said, "it's not my fault."

The ball game was temporarily out of the way. I closed in on Dave.

"Suppose people ate horses," I said.

Dave kept smacking his fist into the hollow of

his glove. "There you go supposin' again," he said.

"And suppose that instead of selling Frank and Bill to pull the moving van, the firemen sold the horses to the butcher. Would you eat Frank and Bill?"

"You're crazy. People don't eat horses."

"They do in France."

"Yeah. Maybe they do. But this is the United States of America. And besides, yum yum, I like hamburgers. Meat. Yum yum yum."

"Is that all you got is a stomach? Don't you have any feelings?"

"Oh, you're crazy," Dave said and struck my shoulder with the heel of his hand.

I returned Dave's blow in kind, only I used both my hands—one hand for each of Dave's shoulders. Dave rushed back at me furiously. The shove I'd given him was both insult and challenge. The next moment we were locked in wrestling holds. We were twined around one another like the wisteria that held tightly to our back porch.

"Willie!"

I strained my right eye to the right—the direction from which my name had been shrieked. My right eye was all I could move. Mother had raised the kitchen window, and her head was out of the window.

I managed to get my hand down in back of Dave, and my hand groped for a good soft spot to pinch. The area I found was a half of a cantaloupe in shape. In softness, it beat the pillows Mother made with chicken feathers. I pinched —harder—as hard as I could.

Dave untangled himself from me in the time it took the howl he howled to get out of him.

I heard the kitchen window come down. Mother—I knew—was on her way. I ran, laughing, very pleased with myself. I could run awfully fast. Dave could never catch me. I slapped my thigh. I became horse and rider. My thigh was the horse, my hand the whip. It was a black cowboy horse I rode. His name was Gunpowder. Nobody in the world could catch me when I was on Gunpowder.

Dave didn't catch me.

The next day when he said he had something to tell me, I thought he wanted to get close to me so that he could return the pinch I had given him.

"Oh, no you don't," I said.

"Honest, Bill," Dave kept saying, "I just want to tell you something."

"Well go ahead and tell me. From where you are. I can hear you. Go ahead."

He didn't want to, but then, finally, he said, "I'm not going to eat any more meat. I decided you were right. People don't treat the dumb animals right. They eat 'em. Just look how they sold Frank and Bill, like Uncle Tom was sold, and now they have to pull that big, heavy moving van."

I was overjoyed at Dave's conversion.

Dave was apprehensive. "Gee, what do you think Mother will say?"

"Don't worry," I said, "I'll tell her. I did it before. I'm used to it."

Before we went to the supper table that night, Mother handed me a surprise.

"Willie, did you eat up half the *nahet* that I made for your supper?" she asked, as though she knew and didn't really have to ask.

"Who, me?" I shook my head violently. "No."

I could see Mother wasn't convinced. When I looked around there was Dave's face; it was a guilty face. Dave had been in the pot of *nahet*. No doubt about it. It wasn't until later that the connection between Dave's gorging himself on the chick peas, rice, and honey and his becoming a convert to vegetarianism occurred to me. It wasn't that the new-found principles had come to make him like meat less; it was just that he found out he liked Mother's meatless dishes more.

Father took my announcement of Dave's decision calmly.

But Mother was worried that my insanity was catching. "Soon," she predicted, "nobody in the family will want to eat meat."

Mr. Josephs didn't stop eating. "Not me," he said, bent over the table, and chewing and swallowing awfully fast the way he always did.

Of course Mr. Myerson didn't say anything.

And I was wondering why Father was so calm. He shouldn't have been. Mr. Myerson didn't eat any meat because of his stomach which was because of his drinking too much. Mr. Josephs was eating my portion of the three pounds of meat Father received free. But now that Dave wasn't going to eat meat any more, there would still be a portion of meat going to waste.

Father said to Mother, "It's far better that the children should have principles that we don't agree with than that they should have no principles at all."

I looked at Father. Suddenly I knew what he was thinking. I hadn't defeated him yet, after all.

Mother was looking at Father, too. We both knew how his mind worked. "Don't!" Mother exclaimed, and I knew she meant, "Don't think of getting me another boarder!"

"What do you mean?" Father asked.

Father's face was completely relaxed and serious—it was Father's innocence-face.

"You know very well what I mean," Mother said, with great assurance.

"Did I say something?" asked Father.

"You looked something," Mother answered.

The boarder Father got was a salesman. He sold powdered eggs.

# SEVEN

Sy argued with Father about nudist colonies. He was all for them.

"So what do you want?" Father asked excitedly. "You want men and women to—to run around without any clothes on?"

Of course that was what Sy wanted. If you knew Sy—he was my oldest brother, and his name was really Sam—I mean, if you really understood him, you could predict what side of any argument he would take.

"That boy will end up on the gallows," Father prophesied time and time again. "Mark my word." He didn't mean this literally or figuratively. He didn't mean it at all. He really believed Sy was so smart and so wonderful that he might end up as President of the United States.

But just the same Sy was always making Father blush.

I remember, when I was especially young, I'd get as close to Father as I could to see if his face was red under his beard. After several attempts to find out, I gave up. Father's beard was too thick. And Father didn't stand still long enough.

But I knew Father loved Sy in spite of all the *agmusnefesh* Sy caused him. *Agmusnefesh* was the Hebrew word Father used in connection with Sy. It meant torture or anguish of the soul.

And Father was very proud of Sy. He was always telling us of Sy's early exploits—those before our time.

"Do you know that he had a letter published in the *Zanesville Sunday News?*"

"Sure," I said. "Sure I know. You told me a killion times, so I ought to know."

This letter of Sy's was in defense of the American Indian, and against the pioneers, and against the reservations.

It was such things as this letter that made people in Zanesville think Sy was too smart for his own good. They meant Sy was crazy.

I didn't think he was. There were quite a few crazy people in Zanesville, really crazy people, but Sy wasn't anything like them. There was Train Engine Joe who thought he was a locomotive. He never walked; always ran, because running was closer to the speed of a train than walking. His right arm moved like a train's piston, and he made the sound of a train as he ran and of a train's whistle when he crossed a street. And then there was Nellie Scallie. She cackled and looked like a witch. Even her name sounded crazy.

The closest Sy came to being like Train Engine Joe and Nellie Scallie was the time he told me feathers were growing out of his head instead of hair. "See," he said, holding up a soft little chicken feather between his thumb and forefinger. "I just picked this out of my head."

But I didn't believe Sy. I was sure he was just joking. No, even with feathers sprouting out of him, Sy wasn't crazy.

Still I was thankful for Father's oft-repeated and reassuring, "That boy's got a good head on him."

Sometimes, however, I'd enjoy thinking Sy was crazy. I'd lie in bed thinking it, enjoying it.

Sy was the craziest man in the world, and I was his brother, I would think. Men in blue uniforms trimmed with gold often came to tie him up and take him away, but I always fought them off and saved Sy. One punch for each man in his blue uniform was all it took. My punches were powerful.

Sy was the craziest man in the world in this fantasy of mine, because he was for the American Indian. I knew more about Indians than he did, I thought, because I went to more movies. Most Indians were halfbreeds. All of them shot burning arrows into covered wagons.

But crazy or not, pro-American Indian though he was, I liked Sy as much as Father did. I was as much in awe of him, too.

Sy fit into each year in exactly the same way. When summer came, Sy came. Throughout my youth Sy was away at school, and so I knew

Sy in no other season of the year except summer
—when he came home for vacation. All the rest
of the time I—and the rest of the family—
knew Sy only by the letters he wrote home.

Sy used big words in his letters. Once he used
the word *rifacimento*.

Father came into the kitchen with the letter.
"What's *rifacimento*?" Father asked Mother.

"*Ri-facimento*?" Mother was up to her elbows
in a pan of dough. She didn't stop struggling
with the dough. "Why don't you write to Sam
and ask him? He would know."

Father started to say it was Sy who had used
the word in a letter, so how could he write to
him and ask him what the word meant; but he
didn't finish, he started to laugh instead.

"It's a good idea," Father said. "I'll do it." He
struck his fist decisively into the palm of his
hand. "Maybe that'll stop him from using such
words in letters."

Just the same Father and all of us were in
awe of Sy's vocabulary.

One summer, I remember, Sy boasted that he
knew every word in the dictionary.

"I'll bet you don't," I said, and got the dictionary from Father's study.

The dictionary was red. The salesman who
sold it to Father said its covers were genuine
leather imported from the south of Morocco.
When the covers started to wear and peel at
the corners, Father said that the covers weren't

genuine leather, but they were imitation paper.

I opened the imitation paper covers quickly. I'd find a word a mile long, and Sy wouldn't know what it meant. I passed by a lot of words because they were too stubby.

*Arborescence* was the word I picked. Sy smiled. He rattled off the exact definition the dictionary gave.

"Ask him a word that begins with z," Dave suggested. "Those are tough ones."

I turned to the back of the dictionary. There was *zaptiah, zax, zeal, zealot.* "What's zealot?"

"You're not serious," Sy said. "That's so easy." And it was. For him.

But Sy wasn't just bookish—or wordish. He liked people and liked to be with them. But most of all he enjoyed seeing their reactions to what he said and did.

So, though Sy liked people, he obviously didn't like them the way Father did.

For example, Father would never tell a woman that her month-old baby looked like a parboiled monkey. Sy did. I was with him when he did.

Shirley Rosen shouldn't have stopped wheeling her baby carriage, but should have gone right by Sy and me with a smile and a hello-how-are-you.

She stopped, however, and pushed the hood of the carriage all the way back so Sy and I could get a complete view of her first-born daughter.

"Isn't she the beautifulest little child?" she asked.

"Looks precisely like a parboiled monkey to me," Sy said.

Shirley Rosen's proudly beaming face collapsed. She gasped futilely for words. The speed with which she left us might possibly have been appropriate for her; it certainly wasn't for the baby carriage.

I wondered if Shirley would tattle on Sy. Should Shirley tattle, I wondered what Father would say to Sy.

"It's that H. L. Mencken," Father lectured Sy after Shirley had tattled. "He's become your God. And now here you are acting the way he writes."

"After this, mothers won't ask me questions," Sy said. "They'll know they can't be certain of the customary endearing stock answers."

Sy's unruffled calm disturbed Father.

"But don't you see that you hurt the woman?" Father asked.

Sy tried to change the subject. He said that mothers were too tied up emotionally with their children. That bringing up children was entirely too haphazard an affair. That children were a distinct species that adults couldn't begin to understand. That . . .

"Will you call her up and apologize?" Father asked.

"What will she expect me to say? Of course, I mustn't say what she doesn't expect."

"Apologies mean a lot to people. Why, I've never been able to understand. You won't have to explain. Simply apologize. And after this don't tell the truth when a lie suits best."

I knew I would have been scared to death to apologize to Shirley Rosen, but Sy wasn't. It didn't bother him much more than a fly.

Sy had as much nerve as the ocean has water. One Saturday night I went around to just about all the fish stores in Zanesville with Sy. He had a little game he was playing with them.

Sy would ask them if they had any dry fish, and when they said they had, Sy would say, "Well, give them a drink."

I went along with Sy, but I didn't go very far into the fish stores with him. I stayed very close to the door while Sy asked his question and gave the funny answer.

Near the door proved the smart place to be.

One fish man didn't have a sense of humor. When Sy said, "Well, give them a drink," he came from around the counter at Sy. He grabbed a fish on the way. A fish as hard and flat and big and dry as a board.

He held the fish in both hands and swung it back and forth in front of him, advancing implacably all the while.

He stopped just outside of his store and shouted at us. I didn't hear what he said; I was too far down the street.

This prank of Sy's was important to me, for it

was indicative of his versatility. His interests were so all-inclusive that even the practical joke was not beneath him.

Music was one of his greatest interests. He was always playing the piano—though he had never taken a lesson. He played from elephant-size music books that he took out of the library.

Mother complained about his playing. "He's always pompyean, pompyean, pompyean."

Pompyean was onomatopoetically descriptive of Sy's playing; criticism, too. Mother reacted to Sy's playing exactly as she did to Mr. Myerson's screechings on the cello.

Mostly, Sy played Chopin.

Chopin—the imperfect way Sy played Chopin —was the musical accompaniment of many of my summers. It was as much a part of those summers as the hot sweet smell of gypsum weed, the hot dust of roads between my toes, the hours spent lying contemplatively in shaded, cool grass.

Sy was enraptured by his playing. When I'd look into the living room, Sy's torso would be weaving to the rhythm of the music. He'd always put his eyes close to the page when he'd make a mistake. It was as though all he had to do was place his eyes directly on a very difficult passage in order to play it.

Sy didn't talk to me very much. At times I thought it was because he was so much older, but Father was even older and he talked to me more than Sy did. But Sy read more than he talked or listened.

The books Sy read weren't just story books, either. He'd read a book on chemistry, one on physics, astronomy, harmony, Harry Elmer Barnes' *Genesis of the World War,* Green's *Short History of the English People.* He'd read several books at once. He'd be in the middle of a book on old American glassware and suddenly decide he must learn Italian and get an Italian grammar and start learning Italian.

One of the firemen, when we lived next to the fire station, warned Sy he'd wear out his eyes. "What you want to take that chance for?" he added. "You only got one set of eyes—and you'll never be given another set. I'm not readin'; I'm takin' care of my one set of eyes."

When Sy stopped reading or playing Chopin, and spent time with me, I was very happy. I more than liked Sy; I suppose it was hero-worship I felt for him. Summer's coming meant the end of school and the arrival of Sy—there was therefore nothing more wonderful in all the world than summer.

But Father preferred the beginning of school to the end. Our home was quieter during school than during vacation. Father thought an awful lot of quiet.

And though Father had his hands full with Sy, he was glad when Sy came home.

Mother was glad, too. Sy said she was the

only one who could cook certain things. She put a lot of onions in her hamburger and very few bread crumbs and Sy liked that.

Father told Sy, "Just be sure she knows you like her cooking and you'll be able to pompyea on the piano both day and night."

Once Father bought a vase, decorated by three nude figures. The vase was a duck's-head green; the nudes orange.

I can't imagine Father saying to the salesman, "I want that vase." He was too shy.

The salesman must have sold the vase to him.

Sy took the vase down, held it in his hands. He turned the vase and looked at the orange nudes, one after the other.

"Did you buy this?" he asked Father. He knew perfectly well Father had; he was just out to have a good time with Father.

Father nodded a yes to Sy's question. His smile was self-consciousness; his red face embarrassment.

Sy laughed to himself. "Since when have you gone in for unclothed females? I'm really surprised. It seems a bit incongruous. A man of God—and this—this secular, mundane, worldly . . ."

"All right! All right! That's enough!"

Father had to cry out as he did in order to check Sy's flow of adjectives before it arrived at a noun. I could tell Father was sure the noun would be a terribly immoral one.

"You've really surprised me," Sy said.

Father snatched the vase from Sy's hands. He put it back on top of the china closet, quickly, decisively.

"It's a design," Father said. "So there's nothing wrong about it. It's a design."

"You rationalize beautifully," Sy said. "What's wrong? Why has your face suddenly turned that sky-blue pink?"

Father had to leave the room to escape from Sy. "So I rationalize beautifully," Father said, and walked quickly from the room.

The nudes were a solid opaque orange, and so lacking in detail they were hardly nudes at all.

Father was right, I thought. You couldn't see anything. So they must be just designs.

This incident was the least of the trouble Sy caused Father.

Sy made the members of the congregation talk. Because of a girl.

One day I saw Sy walking across the Fifth Street bridge with her. Blonde and buxom and blue-eyed. The silk print she wore made her even more buxom. And Sy was tall and student-thin and that made her even still more buxom.

It was the first time I'd ever seen the girl. She looked all right to me. She was pretty. Just a little too big—that was all.

The Friday evening after the day I saw the

girl, I heard the talk. In front of the synagogue, just before the Friday evening service started.

When the weather was nice, there were always a few early arrivals who would stand out in front of the synagogue and talk.

Father was inside at the time, fixing the *Torah*. The *Torah* was a scroll made of sheepskin. The whole Five Books of Moses were written on the scroll, by hand, in ink. Father almost always wound the *Torah* to the right place on Friday night, so it would be ready for the Saturday morning service.

The three men in front of the synagogue were whispering about Sy and the girl whom I had seen on the Fifth Street bridge.

I'd been helping Father fix the *Torah*. And just as I reached the door of the synagogue I stopped because I heard the whispering, and I stayed stopped when I heard what the whispering was about.

They were whispering that there was no reason for Sy's going out with a girl who wasn't Jewish. It was a shame, they said. There were plenty of nice Jewish girls. No excuse for it at all. And they agreed that Sy's behavior might be due to his studying too much.

Hearing them whisper, the way they were whispering about Sy, made me angry. I'd make them stop, I decided. I clenched my teeth hard and stepped out of the door, where I had been standing.

The three men moved apart and quit whispering as soon as they saw me.

I just stood there and looked at them. They moved closer together then and talked—they talked now, didn't whisper.

Father often urged me to come to him if I needed any help or advice. Still I did a lot of thinking about the men and their whisperings, and a lot of hesitating before I went to see him in his study. It wasn't until Monday that I went to see him.

"That girl Sy's going with is a person, isn't she?" I asked Father abruptly.

"What girl? What are you talking about? If she's a girl she must be a person."

I told Father about the three whisperers.

I told Father that Sy once said to me, "I never ask a girl what her religion is. If she interests me and is a genuine person that's all that concerns me."

And, finally, I asked Father if Sy wasn't right and the whisperers wrong.

Father put his hand on top of my head and twisted my cap on top of my head, affectionately, and smiled down at me.

"You're a good boy, Willie," he said.

I waited, wanting an answer to my question.

The smile went off Father's face and just seriousness was there.

"Of course Sy is right," Father said. "He has a mighty good head on him. What a person is comes first; his religion second. I've no doubt that this girl, about whom they whispered, is a very fine girl. Sy's no fool. He wouldn't pick any other kind."

"She's pretty," I said. "She's a little heavy, but she's pretty."

"Your brother Sy's not an ordinary person. He has more than a trace of genius in him."

"Yeah," I said. "I guess he is a genius. He's not plain like most people."

It occurred to me that most people were like Mother's sponge cake—just plain—but that Sy was like Mother's strudel.

Before I left Father's study, Father winked, closing both his eyes, and told me not to tell Mother anything about our conversation. "It will disturb her," he explained.

Bob, Dave, and I figured out a name to call Sy because he was a genius. We called him a blue light.

A blue light was the best name we could think of for pure intellect. The color was somehow just right. And intellect and illumination went well together, too.

To be a blue light, one had to be more than smart. Father was smart, but we never thought of him as a blue light. Father's approach to life was not subtle and complicated; Sy's was, and that made him a blue light.

Take oatmeal at breakfast time. Father said a

blessing and ate it and that was the end of the oatmeal.

But Sy—I can't forget how he stood over boiling oatmeal, more than once, marveling.

*"Just look at it!"* Sy shouted at me.

I hurried to the stove and looked into the pot, expecting to see something at least as great as a rainbow or a crocodile.

"It's as though it were something alive!" Sy went on raving. "It's breathing. It's panting with exertion."

"That's because there's hardly any more water left," I said.

"Listen to the sound it makes. It's a wonderful sound."

"It looks like—like a volcano erupting," I said, slightly excited now by Sy's enthusiasm.

"Its sound range is extremely varied. It's easy to understand how peoples have worshiped inanimate objects. Just listen to it."

"It's done," I said. "Turn off the gas."

I told Father about Sy and the oatmeal.

"All God's works are wonderful," Father said. "Too many people don't realize that. Sy can look in a pot of oatmeal and see God. That boy's got a good head on him."

Gosh, I thought, Father sounds like a blue light.

I knew he was wrong about Sy seeing God in the oatmeal.

Sy never prayed.

And once Sy said, "Monotheism is all right, but it isn't quite fair to the other gods. There surely must be at least two. One of good; one of evil."

And then there was the time Sy went to join the YMCA, and what he said to the Secretary of the YMCA when the Secretary asked him his religion.

"Fireworshiper," Sy said. "I'm a fireworshiper."

I was with Sy when he said it. It frightened me. I wasn't sure if he were joking or not, and if he weren't joking, then maybe Sy was really crazy and I didn't want Sy to be really crazy. Lying in bed and imagining Sy's being crazy was different from Sy's really being crazy.

The Secretary of the YMCA came to see Father about it. His name was Mr. Malakin. His face was bony and pale; not round and rosy like Father's. And he was tall and skinny—holy looking, I thought. His face was still paler when he asked Father if Sy were really a fireworshiper.

Father's chuckle sounded squeezed out. "The boy's a fireworshiper like I'm a—a I don't know what," Father said.

A little color came into Mr. Malakin's face.

I was glad, too. Sy probably said what he said because he was a blue light. He probably wanted to observe Mr. Malakin's reaction—wanted to see his face turn pale. No, I decided, Sy wasn't crazy; he was just a blue light.

# EIGHT

FATHER would never skip prayers. And he wouldn't even cheat a little and shorten them. That was terribly hard to understand when you were eight or nine or ten years old—or even eleven.

It was especially bad on Passover.

There was the *seder,* an interminable ritual, which Father had to finish before we could eat.

"It's a good thing he can read Hebrew fast as lightning," Dave said to me, "otherwise we'd be up all night."

In spite of Father's speed, we'd fall asleep at the table, and when we were roused to eat, we'd chew slowly and our eyes would scarcely be open. And we'd miss the Angel Elijah every time. For the Angel Elijah always came very late to drink the goblet of wine set aside for him.

Passover celebrated the exodus of the Children of Israel from slavery in Egypt. It was a sad holiday and yet a joyous one. It brought to mind centuries of slavery, and also told of deliverance and freedom.

I decided that Father didn't skip any of the *seder* because he wanted us to know what slavery in Egypt was really like.

There were the bitter herbs on the table, and the hard-boiled eggs in salt water which were to remind us that slavery was bad. And the *charoses*, symbolic of the mortar the slaves used in making bricks for King Pharaoh. It was made of apples, nuts, cinnamon and wine, all mixed together. *Charoses* was red, but I never thought that it looked like mortar. There were all these things and still Father didn't skip.

Passover was hard on everyone—especially Mother. I guess you might say she experienced the holiday in its fullest sense because she worked like a slave.

Before the holiday arrived, she cleaned the house with a phobia-like thoroughness. The house wasn't just dusted, it was washed. She did everything short of flushing our home with a hose.

I thought it foolish and unnecessary and I told Father so.

"It's the only way to be sure," Father said, very patiently, "that there's no *chometz* in the house."

*Chometz* was the villain that had to be eradicated. *Chometz* was yeast. The slaves in Egypt didn't have any yeast so we couldn't. We ate matzos, which was unleavened bread. And Mother, because of *chometz*, had to clean the house so thoroughly that there wouldn't be a single bread crumb in the whole house.

*Chometz* was so terrible that we had to use different dishes for Passover. They were kept in a barrel in the cellar. Bringing up the barrel was exciting. What was even more fun was taking the dishes from the newspapers in which they had been wrapped the preceding year.

As if Passover in itself weren't exciting enough, once during the holiday a burglar broke into our house. We were living on Monroe Street then.

The burglar climbed up onto the roof of a side porch; then boosted himself through a window into Mother and Father's bedroom.

Mother always claimed, as though it were an accomplishment worthy of praise, that she was an extremely light sleeper. Father said—jokingly, of course—that when Mother made bread, her sleep was disturbed all through the night by the sound of the dough rising in the breadpan.

Mother must really have been a light sleeper. But the poor burglar had no way of knowing that.

The burglar was straddling the window sill, when Mother screamed. That scream stopped at every house on Monroe Street and woke practically everyone up.

When Sy was told about the power of Mother's scream, in Father's very next letter to him, he wrote, "No wonder she screamed the

way she did. This crook might have been bringing some *chometz* into the house."

I don't think Mother was worried about that.
She undoubtedly was worried that this menac-
ing silhouette on the window sill would take
something of value *out* of the house. But first—
and this was an axiom as far as Mother was
concerned—everybody would be murdered in his
bed.

When we children came dashing onto the
scene, Father was looking out of the open window and Mother was shouting that he do something. All the lights in the bedroom were on.
Father looked funny in his nightgown; he was
short, but it was shorter.

"Go next door!" Mother's voice was shrill. "Go
to the fire station! Call the police!"

"Maybe it's nothing. Maybe you just imagined
it."

"Imagined? I heard him! I saw him! Why
are you standing there?" She must have suddenly realized that she wasn't doing anything
either. "I'll go then! Somebody has to go!"

But Mother didn't have to make the call to
the police; the firemen next door made it. They
were all up. It wasn't because of Mother's
scream; it was because of Father's sacramental
wine.

Father gave the firemen sacramental wine at
Passover time, but the way they handled it, it
became secular awfully fast. Father gave them

the wine because the firemen called him to the telephone in the fire station, and also because they liked the wine so very much. We didn't have a telephone of our own.

"What's the matter, Revner?" one of the firemen shouted up to the bedroom window. (The firemen without exception pronounced Reverend, Revner.)

"My wife claims she saw . . ."

Mother pushed Father aside and stuck her head out of the window. "I don't claim anything!" she screamed. "You call the police—at once! A man climbed right through this window. I saw him. He'd have murdered us right in our beds if I hadn't screamed."

Tim O'Rourke started off at a trot. He was so big he didn't look as if he could run, but he could.

"Tim'll put the call in to headquarters," a fireman explained to Mother. His tone of voice implied that the burglar didn't have a chance now.

Then the firemen started carrying on as if they were at a picnic. They talked very loud and laughed a lot and even sang a little. None of them were wearing their coats. Looking down from the window I couldn't see their faces very well, and since they all had on blue shirts and suspenders, they looked alike.

Only one of them seemed concerned about the burglar. He lay down on his face and stomach and started wriggling under the porch.

Mother didn't like the way the firemen were "carrying on." She even thought that looking under the porch was ridiculous.

"By this time," Mother said, "that burglar is probably in a freight car and on his way to Columbus."

"So he won't bother us," Father said.

"He won't bother us. But do you want to allow such a man to be running loose? He can bother someone in Columbus, can't he?"

"How do you know he's 'such a man'?"

"Didn't he climb through the window? If he's the honest man you're trying to make out, what business does he have climbing through a window—and at night?"

I could see Father was on the burglar's side. I was reading *Les Misérables* at the time, and Father at once became Monseigneur Bienvenu, the kindly bishop who let the crook run off with his silver plates. Mother was Javert, the nerveless police inspector, advocate of the letter of the law.

"Maybe the man was hungry and just wanted a loaf of bread," I said, still under Victor Hugo's influence.

Sophie giggled. "Bread in a bedroom. Whoever heard of bread in a bedroom?"

"He wouldn't even find any in our kitchen now," Bob said. "Bread is *chometz*. The worst you can imagine."

The police arrived. Two policemen. Both tall

and thick through the shoulders; both gripping night sticks.

Father said, "I don't like this at all. That I be the cause of a man being pursued like an animal."

Mother expelled air through her nostrils, wearily. And her shoulders lifted and fell.

I didn't understand what Father meant. The policemen weren't pursuing the burglar as if he were an animal. They talked to the firemen. They looked up at the window. They walked around the house. Then one of them called up to Father (we were all of us still grouped around the window) and asked him if anything had been stolen.

"Nothing," Father shouted back eagerly. "Not so much as a crumb."

Father probably said, "not so much as a crumb," because of what I had just said about the thief wanting a loaf of bread.

Anyway, Father was certainly glad to see the policemen go. I wasn't; I liked the excitement of their being there.

But there were so many things like that that I enjoyed and Father didn't.

In the spring, the Muskingum River gorged itself with rain and threatened to flood its banks. I'd go down to the Y Bridge then and look at the river and hope there would be a flood. Mud made the river look like coffee with too much cream in it. I wanted that coffee to pour into the streets of Zanesville. Schools would close. Men would paddle around the streets in boats. Houses would float away.

Father didn't want any of that. He said special prayers so it wouldn't happen. He spoke earnestly for flood control.

Since Father felt the way he did, I never said out loud that I wanted a flood to happen. I even thought it would be bad if it happened. But I hoped it would.

Could it possibly be, I wondered, that Father didn't hope just a little little bit that a flood would happen?

But I was sure Father was glad to see the policemen go that night. They left with the firemen, who were still quite noisy because they'd been drinking so much sacramental wine.

It was that very same Passover, just two days after "the robbery," that Father had further dealings with the police.

One morning at the synagogue someone told Father that a Jewish man had been arrested for vagrancy.

Father shook his head. It looked like he was groaning—the way he shook his head.

"I'll have to see what I can do," he said. "For him to be in jail is a shame. Such things shouldn't be."

I knew Father meant that this man in jail should be out, and setting an example. Jewish people had to be extra good. Just good wasn't good enough. Being in jail, this man wasn't even being just good.

Father was also especially concerned that this man should be in jail during the Passover holiday.

"You know," he reminded me, "this is a holiday symbolic of freedom.

"Sure," I said, with a cocky pride because I knew, "this is when the slaves down in Egypt were let loose."

"Exactly."

"But a prisoner in jail is not the same as a slave."

Father's attention was far from what I had just said. "And what do you think that poor man's eating in jail? You can be sure he doesn't even get a piece of matzo."

Matzo was bread, really big flat crackers, without any yeast in it. No salt either. The slaves got out of Egypt in a hurry; they didn't have time to put yeast or salt in their bread.

And we couldn't have butter on our matzo, for butter was *chometz*.

Mother said she didn't know what was the matter with Father, when he told her he was going to take matzo to the man in jail.

"It's the very least I can do," Father said. "It's a shame, a Jew in prison. It gives the Jewish people a black eye."

Father wrapped up a five-pound box of matzos.

Bob, Dave, Sophie, and I stood around him, begging him to take us to the jail with him.

"Please—please . . ."

"You think going to jail is a party with ice cream?" Father asked.

"I want to see what it's like," Dave whined.

"It's not for children to see," Mother said.

Sophie started to cry. That with all the rest made an awful racket.

Father didn't like noise at all. He demanded that there be quiet. And Mother said that she wouldn't have any of her children going to a jail. Sophie cried worse than ever. And Bob and Dave continued to resort to entreaty and argument.

I, however, evolved a plan.

No sooner did my father leave the house, than I sneaked into the kitchen and sneaked out with a quart jar full of chicken soup and matzo balls. I could just get three of the balls in the jar, that's all that would fit in.

I ran down the alley—it was a shortcut—and met Father coming down the street.

"I brought some soup and matzo balls for the man in jail," I said, holding up the quart jar for Father to see. The balls were yellow, but the soup was even yellower.

"Hmm, that's very good."

"Can I carry it for you?" I asked. I hesitated before I went on; I was afraid of what Father's answer might be to my next question. "Can I give it to the man in jail?"

"All right," Father consented, without any opposition at all. "Come. I don't mind one person coming, but I couldn't bring the whole family. It would have looked foolish."

"What did this man in jail do?" I asked Father as we walked along.

"Do? You mean why is he in jail? He was arrested because he was a vagrant."

I didn't know what a vagrant was. I didn't ask because it was pleasant to act as if I were smart and knew. This gave me more pleasure, I thought, than knowing could ever give me.

I decided, intuitively, that a vagrant was a fiend. And a fiend was someone who was a criminal just for the fun of it.

The man in jail didn't look anything at all like a fiend.

Father went right into the cell, and I went right along behind him, close behind him.

The door of the cell was made of long iron bars. I thought they would be good to chin yourself on, if they ran the other way, instead of up and down.

"*Sholom alechem,*" Father said, and shook the hand of the man in jail. The man didn't say anything, so Father handed him the box of matzos. "Some matzos," Father said. "You know, of course, that this is Passover?"

The man was very big and broad. His hair was black, wild-looking too, because it wasn't combed.

"My name's O'Malley," the man said and shook Father's hand again. "You must be the Jew rabbi here in town."

They'd finished shaking hands, and the man put a hand to his chin as though he were about to stroke a beard. It was his way of telling Father how he knew Father was a rabbi.

O'Malley was not a typically Jewish name. And the expression Jew rabbi was a non-Jewish redundancy.

Father must have added those two facts together, for he said, "You're not Jewish?" and he shook his head as he asked the question.

"No sir." And O'Malley shook his head as he answered.

The guard, a white-haired man with a lot of keys, stood in the corridor listening.

"But you speak the Jewish lingo, don't you, O'Malley?" the guard asked. "You can rattle it right off, can't you?"

O'Malley smiled, "*Ich ken reden mamma loshen zehr gut,*" he said, and he said it fast.

Father looked perplexed. "But if you're not Jewish, how is it that you can speak . . . ?"

"Hung around Jews all my life," O'Malley explained. "Worked with 'em. Over in Covington, 'cross the river from Cincinnati. Picked up a lot of Jewish words, working with 'em."

O'Malley started going through his repertoire. The words he knew fell under one or the other of two headings: Swear. Dirty.

Father tried to pretend he didn't know any of the words by wrinkling his brow. But both his cheeks were red. And I knew that not understanding something would never do that to your cheeks, but that understanding would.

"Will you excuse me?" Father said to O'Malley. He walked to the door of the cell. "I'll be back shortly."

At first I thought Father was escaping from O'Malley's vocabulary. Then my imagination went to work and explained Father's departure in terms far more dramatic.

O'Malley, I decided, was the silhouette mother had seen on her bedroom window sill. O'Malley was the one who was going to murder all of us in our beds.

"When did you come to Zanesville?" I asked O'Malley.

"Blew in the day before yesterday."

That was the day of "the robbery."

O'Malley was seated on the cell's cot, and I was standing before him. O'Malley was eating the matzo balls. He speared chunks of the balls out of the jar with a long-bladed pen knife. He'd chew a little bit and then take a drink of the cold soup, holding the jar in both his hands.

I decided I had better keep talking to O'Malley so Father would have ample time to call the police. I didn't permit the fact that O'Malley was already imprisoned and the police right on the premises to spoil my imaginings.

"You like matzo balls?"

O'Malley's mouth was full. He smiled, nodded, winked.

"Don't you get tired just staying in here?"

"Man, oh man, oh man and that's not all."

"You get lonesome, too?"

"I got me a woman and a boy big as you over in Covington."

"Does your boy who's as big as me know you're in jail?"

"Nah." O'Malley stopped eating. He put the jar down on the floor. His arms hung limp, dejected. His wild black hair made the whole of O'Malley looked neglected and uncared for.

I felt awfully sorry for O'Malley and his little boy. I thought how terrible it would be if Father were a vagrant in jail and I were away off in Covington.

I heard steps out in the corridor. I hoped Father hadn't told the police O'Malley was the one who had tried to rob our house.

The white-haired guard opened the door with his keys and let Father in.

I hurried over to Father and announced, "Mr. O'Malley has a boy as big as me over in Covington."

I felt that if Father knew this fact he wouldn't have O'Malley arrested again. If he were arrested again, while he was still in prison, he would never get out of prison.

"You know what *mazel tov* means?" Father asked O'Malley.

"Got me there," O'Malley answered.

"*Mazel tov.* Congratulations. That's what it means. I'm going to get you out of prison. I just talked to Chief Tomlinson. A fine man. He said if I got you a job and was responsible for you . . ."

"Can you get him a job?" I asked. I was delighted—just a little anxious.

"Certainly," Father said. He was a little uncertain, because he then said, "Why not?" emphatically.

O'Malley shook hands with Father again. This was the third time. He laughed. "*Zehr gut,*" he said. "*Zehr gut.*"

The next thing Father did was to take a small package out of his pocket. It was a quarter of a pound of butter. He'd talked to Chief of Police Tomlinson and bought the butter. Jewish people didn't eat their matzos with butter, because the slaves in Egypt hadn't any butter for their matzos. Besides, it was *chometz.* But O'Malley wasn't really Jewish. He just knew some Jewish words.

"Here's some butter for your matzos, Mr. O'Malley," Father said, smiling happily. "You might as well enjoy them."

# NINE

ZANESVILLE'S Main Street had a cemetery at one end, circus grounds at the other. Father said it was symbolic, that he must use it in a sermon some time. But he never did.

Still, cemeteries were the locale of a lot of work Father had to do.

"I marry them and bury them," Father often said with a sad chuckle. Then he'd hasten to add that those two tasks were just a small part of his job.

I didn't really think about death very much until Marvin died. It was while I was in the seventh grade. Marvin was bigger and older than I, and that and other things made me like him more than all the other fellows put together. He was fourteen. Always laughing. And it seemed to me he wasn't scared of anything.

Marvin had a Harley-Davidson motorcycle. When he went around corners, he slanted halfway to the street. He traveled at least a mile a minute.

One morning when I came to school, I knew right away something was wrong. The fellows weren't playing touch football in the school yard. They were standing around talking.

Marvin had been killed. To avoid a speeding truck at an intersection, he drove his motorcycle into a telephone pole, snipped the pole right off. He wasn't dead then; he died in the ambulance on the way to the hospital.

I didn't believe it. Marvin dead. Killed. I didn't believe it.

Tears came into my eyes. I was concerned that the fellows might see the tears, more concerned that I might start crying out loud and then they'd surely know I was crying. My throat ached. I stretched my neck, but it didn't help, and I couldn't swallow. I felt worse than I'd ever felt in my whole life.

When my dog Shep had died, it was pretty bad. I watched Shep die. He had Saint Vitus. I was down on the ground beside Shep, stroking him, watching him die, and I didn't stop crying for a second.

But Marvin wasn't a dog; he was a boy. He was the first boy I had known who had died. Death was no longer a meaningless word; it was a menace to me, to all my friends, to my father and mother, my brothers and sister. And death wasn't fair. Marvin hadn't done anything wrong. And he wasn't an old man with a white beard who'd lived an awfully long time. Marvin shouldn't have died; it wasn't fair.

But Marvin was dead.

Marvin would never laugh again the way he did.

Marvin would never again go slanting around corners on his Harley-Davidson.

It was impossible and painful to believe.

I remembered the funeral parades I'd seen. They hadn't meant death to me. There was a band and slowly marching men and carriages and a hearse. The hearse was as ornamental as a circus wagon; but it was just gray, not bright red and bright yellow. Bob, Dave, and I would walk along on the sidewalk. It was fun. You only had to be careful not to count the carriages in the procession. If you did, there was certain to be a death in your family. And it was difficult to keep from counting them. But I'd never really thought much about death before; now, because of Marvin, I did.

I went to Marvin's funeral; all the fellows went. Father was there, too. He conducted the services.

Tears—they were something all people had. No matter who or what they were. I knew it was so when I saw Marvin's father cry. He was a huge man, heavy with flesh, mean in his silence. I didn't think he could cry, but he did. The clumps of ground—hard and gray with frost —made him cry, the sound they made when they rolled and hit the coffin his boy was in.

I cried, too. Uncontrollably. As I had cried when Shep, my dog, had died.

Father tried to comfort me that night. He spoke to me about immortality. It didn't help. Marvin's spirit couldn't ride a motorcycle, and if it couldn't do that, it couldn't begin to compare with the mortal part of Marvin that could.

"I don't believe in living after you're dead," I told Father.

"And why not? If life is possible, certainly immortality is—it is no greater a miracle."

"Yeah, but what's the good of it, if your body is dead?" (I was still thinking of Marvin. A spirit now, according to Father, but as a spirit unable to ride a motorcycle.)

"You only know of life with a body," Father persisted. "Can't you imagine a higher form of life, where a body isn't necessary?"

"No, I can't."

Without a body, I thought, you couldn't eat ice cream. Movies were out. And so was walking on street curbs, jumping over sidewalk grates, leaping up to touch the scalloped edge of awnings. Every pleasure I knew was impossible without a body. What could a spirit do that was more fun?

"Why take chances?" my father said, and laughed to cross out what he had just said. "If you can't believe in immortality, act and pray as if it is real."

"But Marvin's dead," I said hopelessly. "What can you do about that?"

Father put his arm around me, and his hand

squeezed my shoulder. That was all the answer he gave me.

Though Father couldn't do anything about Marvin, he did do something about Joel Bernstein. Death had come for Joel Bernstein. Death had already stretched forth a bony hand to take Joel Bernstein.

It was the winter Marvin died that Joel Bernstein took sick. Pneumonia. Double pneumonia.

Joel was studying at Ohio State to be an electrical engineer. He came home for Thanksgiving. It was only fifty-two miles from Columbus to Zanesville so he hitch-hiked. When he arrived home, he was sneezing, just sneezing, but that was the beginning of his double pneumonia.

Joel's mother came to our house one afternoon to see father. She was as short as Father. There was a high pile of gray hair on top of her head, but she was still no taller than Father.

I remember how she sat in a big upholstered chair in our living room. Her handkerchief was balled up and soggy in her hand, and she kept putting the corner of it to her tear-reddened nose and eyes.

"There is no hope. The doctors say there is no hope for my Joel."

Father's face was pale and very serious. He'd circumcised Joel when Joel was a baby. In the coming summer, he was supposed to marry Joel to Charlotte Cohen. I knew Father was thinking that he couldn't possibly bury Joel.

Father said, "Don't give up. Doctors can be wrong.

"But no hope. They said, 'No hope.' "

"Doctors are only human, Mrs. Bernstein. They can make a mistake."

But I was sure Joel Bernstein would die. That the doctors hadn't made a mistake. I couldn't forget Marvin and how he had died.

Marvin had had a dimple in his chin. He didn't have to smile to make it, the way you do with dimples in your cheeks. It was there all the time.

I thought of Marvin's dimple in his chin, and how fast he could go on his motorcycle.

The next morning I awoke before David. I could hear him breathing. The bedroom was completely quiet. There was just the quiet and David's breathing.

I turned and lifted myself a little and looked down on David. His face was chubby; his hair black. I listened to the sound of his breathing. If that sound stopped, David would be dead. The idea that he could cease to exist so easily frightened me.

I eased myself quietly out from under the covers, dressed quickly. Went into the bathroom and washed quickly. I wanted to forget what I had thought, but doing things quickly didn't help.

Father said special prayers in the synagogue

for Joel Bernstein. He went to Joel's home and prayed there too.

Father was pale. He lost weight. It occurred to me that Father was wrestling with the Angel of Death just like Jacob wrestled with the Angel of Death in the Bible.

Father was determined not to let Joel die. He liked Joel and he liked Charlotte Cohen, the girl Joel was supposed to marry.

"Will all these prayers help?" I asked Father.

"We'll see," he said humbly, and his voice was so low it was hardly a whisper.

Joel Bernstein began to improve.

The doctors shook their heads. They couldn't understand it.

Mrs. Bernstein—unlike the doctors—knew what had happened.

She came to see Father. She still touched her handkerchief to her nose and eyes, but her tears were happy tears.

"You straightened it out, Rabbi," she told Father, and though her voice quivered, it was strong with certainty. "You straightened it out with the *Rebono Shelolom*."

*Rebono Shelolom* meant master of the world, and that meant God.

This, I thought, is what Mrs. Bernstein must think: God must have made a mistake, confused Joel with someone else who was scheduled to die, and Father's prayers called the matter to

God's attention and He looked into it, saw the error, and corrected it immediately.

I thought Mrs. Bernstein naive; God wasn't an incompetent bookkeeper who made clerical errors.

Mrs. Bernstein was holding both of Father's hands. She'd dropped her handkerchief, and I moved quickly to pick it up for her.

She was crying and laughing, kissing one of Father's hands and then the other.

She was trying to get down on her knees before Father, at the same time that she was kissing his hands. She was too old, and I guessed it was her corset that was in the way. Besides, Father lifted up her hands and wouldn't let her get down. Father was very embarrassed and begged her to stop.

The inside of my nose stung; my eyes stung. Tears came into my eyes. I felt sorry for Mrs. Bernstein. Not sorry, too, because Joel was going to live.

And I was very proud of Father. He hadn't straightened things out with God the way Mrs. Bernstein believed. But he'd surely done something, something equally effective. The doctors had given Joel up. Then Father arrived. It was like a movie. The Indians, whom Sy had so strangely defended in a letter to the editor, had circled the covered wagons, were shooting flaming arrows into them. But far off in the distance a cloud of yellow dust rose. The cavalry. Father was like the cavalry.

Movies were such an important part of my life that it is not strange I immediately thought of Father in terms of cavalry. And in those days every movie ended with cavalry. And with dust off in the distance.

As Joel Bernstein improved, so did Father. Father's cheeks became rosy. His vest stopped looking like a balloon with the air out of it, but like a balloon with the air in it.

One day I saw Joel Bernstein walking in the street. His face was very white; blue, on the part he shaved. He walked slowly, like the Civil War veteran who was ninety-one and lived on Spring Street.

"You're alive," I said to myself, "because of Father."

Every time I saw Joel after that, that was what I thought.

The following June Father married Joel to Charlotte Cohen. Mrs. Bernstein insisted it be done in our house. I was at the wedding. A canopy was held over Charlotte and Joel during the ceremony. I stood on a chair and held one corner of the canopy.

As soon as Father said the last words of the service, Mrs. Bernstein headed for Father. She wanted to kiss his hands. But Father excused himself and hurried away as if he had to go to the bathroom.

I suppose it was because Marvin died and Joel almost died that I went through a serious period.

Once in the middle of a movie an over-whelming sense of unreality fell upon me. My being there seemed strange. My being there with all these other individuals seemed strange. That we should all be sitting there together in a dark theatre, looking at a movie was unreal, goose-pimply.

These strangers in the movie were alive, just like I was alive. They were just like me. Every-one was. They had a father and a mother; they ate, slept, played, and things happened and those things became their memories. They could tell stories about a school teacher, an accident, a trip they once made, a trip they once wanted to make, an ambition, a quarrel.

I suddenly felt very close to everyone—as though they were all my brothers and sisters. If they were sick, I should take care of them, and if I couldn't do that, I should at least be concerned about them. I should at least say hello to people when I saw them on the street. But could I say hello to everyone? Would they understand? Wouldn't they think I was crazy? Sy might be able to do it, but could I?

These ideas I'm thinking, I thought, are great and majestic. I felt very great and majestic for having thought them. I didn't want to admit to myself that they stemmed from ideas my father had expressed.

I had to talk to Father. I did, that night on the porch. I was sitting on the top step. Father was in a rocker near me. Then came Mother in a rocker. And Dave, Sophie, and Bob were on the porch swing.

It was a summer night and very dark and silent because a storm was on its way. There were lightning bugs flashing all around; in the sky there was real lightning, not quick, tendriled streaks dividing the sky, but flashes of illumination springing from the horizon.

Again I felt the feelings of weird unreality I had felt that afternoon in the movie. Was Father my father; Mother my mother? Were we here, here in this unbelievable world together? How had it happened that my life was so closely interwoven with the lives of these individuals here on the porch, on the two rockers, on the swing?

I thought about this for a long time and then I said, "If the world began with Adam and Eve, just Adam and Eve, then everybody is related, aren't they?"

Father stopped rocking. It was so dark I could hardly see him. "Certainly," Father said. "Certainly."

"Everybody is related then. It doesn't matter whether they are Protestants or Catholics or what they are."

"That's exactly right," Father said. "And if . . ."

Mother interrupted. She didn't stop rocking; she rocked faster. "What are you telling him?" she scolded. "You're going to mix him up."

Just then Bob, Dave, and Sophie started to fight on the swing. It seemed to be a question of who had kicked whom first. There was a lot of noise. I couldn't ask Father any more questions.

I just sat there on the porch, watching the lightning lighting up the sky, majestically oblivious to the noise on the porch. Those silent eruptions of light on the horizon, the velvety darkness, the sultriness promising a storm, all of these things were proper to my cosmic mood.

The very next day I discovered *The Spoon River Anthology* in the library. Its morbidity both frightened and attracted me. Every man, woman, and child became an epitaph. Life was purposeless—a flash of light between interminable darknesses.

Where are Elmer, Herman, Bert, Tom and Charley,
The weak of will, the strong of arm, the clown,
  the boozer, the fighter?
All, all, are sleeping on the hill.*

*The Spoon River Anthology,* by Edgar Lee Masters (New York: The Macmillan Company) © by the author, 1914, 1915, 1916.

"What's the matter with you?" Mother asked me.

"Huh? What?"

"You've been acting half asleep lately. Maybe you need a little castor oil."

"I'm all right."

"You're sure? I've some oranges. Would you take some castor oil if I gave it to you?"

Mother's giving me the castor oil was certainly no inducement; her method was medieval; she'd hold my nose so I wouldn't smell the brimming tablespoon of the stuff as she forced it into my mouth.

Merely visualizing Mother's method made me slightly nauseous.

"Would you take it?" Mother's voice intruded on my thought. "You must need it. You're still standing there like a *golem,* with your eyes half closed."

"I don't need any castor oil. Why don't you ever let me alone?"

"If you don't need castor oil, then only God can help you. I can't. Go out and get some fresh air. I'm busy."

I didn't leave the kitchen. Mother hurried over to a huge pan of bread dough, covered by a tablecloth and a red and black afghan. The dough was running out of the pan and she punched it back. I stood watching her.

Poor Mother, I thought. Poor everybody.

"You're still standing there." Mother's voice again. "Be a good boy, take some castor oil. I'll give you only a teaspoon. I'll get it for you."

As Mother headed for the medicine chest, I walked slowly out of the house. I walked. Mother called to me, but I kept on walking. Here I was thinking of human destiny, of life and death, and Mother thought I needed castor oil. It was tragically funny. How important was this bread Mother felt she had to make. In a thousand years where would the bread be? Where would Mother be and where would I be?

Though I passed out of this slump—within a matter of hours—I couldn't forget about death because Father was always having funerals. But Marvin's funeral was the only one I'd gone to, and I didn't want to go to another one.

Then the meanest man in Zanesville died.

Father told Mother he was worried. "I hope there will be at least a *minyan* at the funeral."

A *minyan* was a quorum of ten. A complete and dignified religious service of any kind required a *minyan*.

"If all of Isaac Rubin's enemies come to his funeral," Mother said sagely, "you'll have more than a *minyan*."

"The man just died," Father reminded Mother. "How can you talk that way?"

"I believe in telling the truth and shaming the devil."

148

Mother often made that statement; it was a favorite of hers. I often wondered what it meant.

That night I went with Father to the home of the late Isaac Rubin. I was scared, but I forced myself to go. Next year I'd be in the eighth grade; then I'd graduate. If I was to understand life, I told myself, I'd have to know more about death.

When I was in the living room containing the coffin, increasing fear dissipated my curiosity. Just the same, I couldn't understand how people could talk and smile in the room with the coffin and the dead man. They spoke a bit lower, but that was all. I felt sorry for the dead man, that he was dead, and—almost—ignored.

Afterwards, when I asked Father about it, he told me that life went on—that to go on was of its very essence. And it went on even in the presence of death.

It still didn't seem right to me.

But Isaac Rubin did have a crowd to see him off at the cemetery. More than a *minyan*.

I stood beside Mother during the funeral service, and she stood right at the edge of the grave. Bob and Sophie were there, too, but Dave wasn't because he was afraid to come. Dave said he had a toothache; but his teeth could have been in my mouth, I was that sure he didn't have a toothache.

Mother let us go to the funeral because she was afraid that there wouldn't be anyone there.

But to look at the crowd you'd think it was a county fair, not a funeral. All of I. Rubin's enemies must have come, just as Mother had said.

I was suddenly worried that Father, in front of all that crowd, might forget his eulogy. I could see how flustered he was by how red his cheeks were.

Behind me a man said, "He was one of those I guys. Everything was I, I, I. Even his name was I. Rubin. The man was infatuated with himself."

I felt sorry for Mr. Isaac Rubin, felt angry too, that such a thing should be said about a man who lay in a coffin, helpless to defend himself.

But I had forgotten about Father. He talked up for Mr. Rubin, the way a lawyer talks up for a client who is being tried.

"You can't judge a person," Father said. "Do you want to know why? Because before you can judge him—accurately, honestly—you must have all the facts behind his so-called misbehavior. That of course is impossible.

"How many of us knew Isaac Rubin? We all knew the superficial aspects of his behavior. Many mistook those for the man. Many were angered because of them. Anger is a convenience; it saves one all the work of understanding why an individual behaves so contrary to our way of thinking.

"Mr. Rubin did not know the love of parents; his home was an orphan asylum. He was never well. He did not have the comfort of a wife and children . . ."

I was awfully proud of the way Father was talking up for Mr. Rubin. I now realized how foolish I'd been to fear that Father might forget his eulogy because of the big crowd in attendance. Father was talking this eulogy the way he talked his sermons. And when you talk to someone, it isn't possible for you to forget or run out of something to say.

"Isaac Rubin was a good man," Father was saying. "He made the mistakes that all of us make. He yearned for the happiness that all of us desire. Cornered by the events of his life, he fought to gain happiness by making money— he thought that that was the way to happiness. He, of course, was wrong. Ironically, however . . ."

Father was just talking. He didn't believe in elocution. And though his talk was pretty fancy at times, it was just the way Father talked.

"Ironically, however," Father was actually smiling as he said this, smiling right there in the cemetery, "this money that he amassed gave him at least several moments of happiness. Unfortunately, those moments of happiness were on his deathbed. He told me, as he lay dying, and there was laughter in his eyes that had too rarely known laughter, that he was giving his money to an orphan asylum in Cleveland. The one on Euclid Avenue in which he had grown up as a boy. 'They need that money,' he said, 'and I'm happy to give it to them.' He said he was happy, mind you. I heard him say that he was happy and I honestly believe that he was.

"There was certainly generosity and nobility in Isaac Rubin's deathbed bequest. There was . . ."

Everybody knew that Mr. Rubin was stingy, a clutcher of pennies. That was why Father had to try and prove them wrong. And he went on and on like that until he'd covered every bad thing about Mr. Rubin and made nothingness of them.

And before Father was through, I heard someone behind me whisper, "Too bad. We certainly lost a good man."

And I thought, golly, he must mean Isaac Rubin.

That night Mother was reading the *Times Recorder*—she always read the morning paper at night because she was too busy to read it during the day.

She stopped suddenly and looked at Father. She stopped so suddenly I heard her stop.

"You know nothing about this advertisement?" she said accusingly.

"Advertisement?" Father asked, opening his eyes wide so he would look innocent.

But he must have known what Mother meant, for he couldn't help smiling the way he did when he had done something he shouldn't have done, like buying a new piece of furniture.

I looked over Mother's shoulder at the paper she held spread wide on her lap.

The advertisement advertised Mr. I. Rubin's funeral. It said Father was going to deliver a eulogy on the subject: I. Rubin—a kindly spirit. It was a square advertisement, with a black line around it. Pretty big, too.

"No wonder you had such a crowd at the cemetery," Mother said.

"It was much more than ten *minyans*," I said.

Father didn't say anything; he was just waiting to hear what Mother would say next.

She said, "A big advertisement like this must have cost plenty." She rustled the paper to indicate the advertisement she meant, and her eyes were angry with Father.

"It didn't cost a penny," Father said quickly. "Hal Pearson, the editor, wouldn't take a penny for it."

"Why?" I asked.

Father smiled, moved his skull cap so it was right on top of his head. "Hal said he couldn't take any money for it. Because I. Rubin—a kindly spirit—wasn't an advertisement. It was news. That's what he said."

## TEN

FATHER claimed Christianity wasn't practical.

"It's a religion that disregards human nature," he said.

But Father was always acting just like a Christian. Turning the other cheek—that sort of thing.

There was the time I found him scrubbing the kitchen floor for old Mr. Schneller.

It was seven o'clock, and Father hadn't yet come home for supper.

"Willie," Mother said, "will you go and see what's wrong with that man?"

She didn't say "your father"; she said "that man," so she was angry.

"I don't want to go away over there," I whined. "Father'll be home soon as he finishes writing a letter for old man Schneller."

"And you can tell that man that for the life of me I can't understand what business he has writing letters for other people."

Father wrote and read letters for Mr. Schneller because Mr. Schneller couldn't write or read. He did the same thing for a lot of other members

154

in his congregation who had come from the old country.

When I arrived at Mr. Schneller's house, no one answered my knock on the front door, so I went around to the back.

As soon as I knocked there, I heard a scuffling and grunting I couldn't understand.

I knocked again.

"Come in!" It was my father's voice. "Come in!"

Father was down on the kitchen floor, on his hands and knees. There was a dirty, wet rag under one of his hands; soap suds and water ⌐ll over the kitchen linoleum.

"Gosh!" I exclaimed. "What are you doing down there on the floor?"

Father didn't answer; he tried to get up. The soap suds on the floor wouldn't let him.

My feet slid on the soap suds too. I tried to pull Father up, but I couldn't. He was heavy. Finally, Father went across the floor on his hands, like a baby, to the kitchen range. He pulled himself up on it; that was how he got to his feet.

"When I went down," Father panted, "I didn't think it would be at all difficult getting up."

"Why are you scrubbing?"

"Mr. Schneller is upstairs. He's not feeling well. The poor man's alone. Someone has to do a little cleaning."

"Mother's very angry," I said. "You're late for supper. She said you had no business writing letters for Mr. Schneller. And, boy, if she were to know about your scrubbing . . ."

Father had started a slow and careful passage across the treacherous kitchen floor, but he stopped. "How will she know I was scrubbing the floor?" he asked. "If no one tells her, she won't know."

I shook my head emphatically. "I won't tell her," I said. I was habitually not telling Mother things.

"Good," Father said. "Now, wipe up the floor like a good boy, Willie. If I get on my knees, I'll have trouble getting up again."

As I finished the work Father had started, I thought Father could be very foolish at times. Who ever heard of scrubbing a floor, if no one told you to do it, or if you weren't paid for doing it?

I knew if Father hadn't told me to wipe the floor, I wouldn't have done it.

I supposed Mother must be right about Father.

"You think it's wrong to be selfish?" I asked Father as we left Mr. Schneller's house and started home together.

"I should say not," Father said without hesitation.

"You don't? But you're not selfish. Why aren't you selfish?"

"But I am selfish."

"Aw."

"I do the things that are to my own interest," Father went on to explain. "I believe that all individuals are important and that includes myself. You should do unto yourself as you should do to others."

"Yeah, but then why did you scrub the floor?" I had Father there.

"Why did I scrub the floor?"

I was sure I had him.

"Well, it struck me as a symbol of something fine. Here was an old and sick man and I came and scrubbed his floor." He chuckled. "Tried to scrub it."

"You mean you scrubbed it just because it was a symbol? It wasn't even dirty or anything?"

"Well, the floor wasn't really in urgent need of cleaning," Father admitted.

"But you did it because it made you feel good to be cleaning old Mr. Schneller's floor?" I asked, slowly, thoughtfully.

"Your mother believes floors never are clean. You can clean them any time. All the time."

At this point Father could not persuade me the floor needed cleaning. I was glad it hadn't needed cleaning and that Father had tried to clean it. Anybody could clean a dirty floor. But to clean a clean floor—significantly—that was another matter altogether. I was accordingly deeply impressed by what my father had done.

The next day, I strolled over to Mr. Schneller's house, strolled because I hadn't decided yet what I was going to do. Besides, I was deep in the fantasy of pretending I was Father. I put my hand to my face and it felt a beard. I thought, "I must hurry, because I haven't even started to prepare my sermon. Why must people have sermon after sermon after sermon . . . ?"

I walked around Mr. Schneller's house, looking for something I could do for the poor old man who lay helpless in bed. I was afraid to go inside, so I confined my looking to the outside of the house.

The spouting that ran like a trough across one end of the back porch caught my eye. It sagged a little; I decided to remedy the sag. It would, moreover, give me a chance to climb onto the roof of the back porch. I liked to climb—as much now, when I was twelve, as when I was younger.

Mother often said, "Don't you climb!"

That she said this, said it often, occurred to me as I climbed the back porch. My climbing also spoiled the illusion that I was Father and not myself. Father couldn't climb. He was too fat. His knees would have hit his belly too soon. But I kept on climbing.

I don't know how my foot slipped, but it did. I grabbed—for anything. My hands would catch the spouting—just where it sagged. And there I was, hanging in the air. The spouting creaked, and I worried that my weight would tear the whole spouting off the roof. I let go.

It wasn't until I'd dropped to the ground that I discovered the bleeding gash over my eye. I put my hand to my head, looked at my fingers and saw the blood. I'd cut my head on the spouting when I'd grabbed hold of it in falling.

I ran, the blood streaming down over my face from my forehead making me run faster. When I was very young, I thought it was essential to life to have every drop of blood that belonged to you in you. My excited state caused me to think that way now. What if all the blood in me ran out before I got home? I ran still faster, sobbing. I had to get home with blood in me, so that I'd be alive. I didn't want to have all the blood out of me and be dead. You could bleed to death.

I thought Father would ask me what happened, but he didn't. He just picked me up in his arms, the way he did when I'd fall asleep at the table after supper and he'd have to carry me upstairs to bed, and he ran out of the house and down the street, holding me that way.

Father took me to Dr. Scott. Dr. Scott was a Socialist and a radical, but Father took me to his office because he was closer to our house than any other doctor.

Afterwards Mother said, "Did you have to go to Dr. Scott?"

And Father answered, "Did you have to ask that question?"

Father would have said something nicer to Mother, but he hadn't yet gotten over the fear that I might bleed to death before he got me to a doctor.

I liked Dr. Scott better than Dr. Fitzgerald, our doctor. Dr. Scott was taller and skinnier, and he was always smiling as if he were having a good time.

All I remember about Dr. Fitzgerald was that he lived in a house on Elberon Avenue, that he vaccinated me when I started school, and that he was always advising people to keep the bad night air out by nailing down the windows good and tight.

That fall—out of thankfulness to Dr. Scott for having fixed my forehead—Father voted the Socialist ticket.

"I thought you were a Democrat," I said to Father.

"I'm a Democrat too," he answered.

"But you can't be both. You can only vote for one. Anybody knows that."

"Dr. Scott is an a-number-one person, Willie. He wants everybody in the world to be happy. And he thinks that if there were fewer poor people in the world, more people, poor and rich, could be happier. He had a long talk with me. There is no question about it, the man is a humanitarian."

"But the Socialists never win. It's either the Republicans or the Democrats."

Father's smile was indulgent. "Remember this," he said. "Don't vote for the one who will win. Vote for the one you want to win."

This sounded very much like scrubbing Mr. Schneller's floor when it didn't need scrubbing.

And I couldn't forget the aftermath of that floor cleaning. My blood had flowed. And Father had to pay two bills—Dr. Scott's and the bill of the roofer whom Father called to repair Mr. Schneller's spouting. Mr. Schneller had wanted to pay the roofer, but Father wouldn't permit him.

I knew what Mother would say to all this. She would say Father couldn't afford the luxury of doing what stood for fine things, if they were going to be *that* expensive.

I once asked Father if we were rich.

"No," Father said.

"But we're not poor."

"No. No, we're not poor."

"What are we then? Are we just right in the middle?"

Father didn't answer my question; he just laughed, and said, "What are you trying to do, bother my head?"

There were a number of things that made me suspect we were really poor, not "just right in the middle." But I never felt poor. And nobody else in our family did.

Of course there were times—many times—I wanted things, but never got them. Above all the things my heart desired and which my hands could not have was an Erector set. Not just a plain Erector set, but an Erector set with a motor. You could make things like windmills and drawbridges and the motor would run them.

I pressed my nose against a cold department store window one Christmas and looked and looked and looked at the Erector set with the motor.

At another holiday season, at Eastertime, I had looked in the window of a confectionery store right next to the interurban station. It was beautiful with chocolate rabbits and eggs. I rested my nose against the cold window. The eggs had writing and designs on them, and the writing had been done with wriggles of colored frosting. If I could just sit down inside that window overnight, I thought, there wouldn't be a rabbit or an egg there in the morning, just me.

Laughter broke into my thoughts. I turned and there was a big, jovial man, wearing a big gray hat. He took me inside and bought me a big Easter egg that had red, white, and green filling inside it. And a rabbit that was just white inside, marshmallow.

It was because of this occurrence that I went and looked at the Erector set with the motor.

Sophie went along. She kept saying, "You

don't look like you want it enough. You won't get it because you don't look like you want it enough."

"Well, I want it," I said, taking my nose from the cold window. "And if it doesn't show through onto my face, it never will."

No saint in a big gray hat came along this time. And I never got the Erector set.

When I told Father about my overwhelming passion, he asked me how much it cost.

"Two ninety-eight," I said.

"Three dollars is a lot of money," Father answered.

"It's not three dollars. It's two ninety-eight."

Father wouldn't be fooled by the calculated euphemisms of merchants. "It's three dollars less two cents," he said. "Well, why don't you save and buy it?"

My daily allowance consisted of one penny. Before Father went away in the morning, he left four pennies on the table in the living room. One each for Bob, Dave, Sophie, and myself.

For six mornings I saved toward the purchase of the Erector set with the motor; then I quit. I felt hollow inside, weak from the strain of discipline. Six whole, long days had gone by, and I hadn't eaten a penny's worth of candy.

I ran to Mrs. Lewis's candy store, the six pennies in my hand. The bell on the door rang as I opened it and went into the store. It rang again as the door closed. The bell sounded awfully good, and it reminded me I hadn't been in the store for six days.

It took a long time deciding what you wanted when you were very young and had a penny to spend, but when you had six, it took at least six times as long and I spent all six of my pennies.

After that experience, the Erector set with the motor was forgotten, collecting dust in my subconscious.

But the Erector set was only one of my desires. I often wished Father didn't have a beard.

"If Father only didn't have a beard," I wished fervently, but silently and guiltily.

I felt guilty about being opposed to Father's beard, for to Father, all that hair around his face was very important. I'm sure, given the choice, he would have preferred losing his right arm to his beard. The Bible said nothing about having your right arm cut off; it said, however, that you should let your beard alone.

Children would often hunch up their shoulders when they saw Father and move their hands at chest level, one over the other. This meant Father talked with his hands, and was therefore Jewish.

This annoyed Father, but he was able to say, "Do you think they know what they're doing? A few years ago they were on the apple tree."

"The apple tree" was Father's way of referring

to the prenatal state. The womb was a word too feminine and biological for Father.

But the gestures of the children hurt me. They made me feel alien, different—and I very much wanted to be accepted in a complete and unqualified sense by everyone.

Once I went on a hike with at least a dozen fellows. We took lunches along. Mother was always worried about my eating enough food so I would have enough strength. Her sandwiches, as a consequence, were robust rather than dainty. Thick slices of bread. Between them, lettuce, to matoes, slabs of cheese.

I had to hold a sandwich with both hands, work hard to get it into my mouth and b e off a corner.

Everyone was down on the grass, eating their lunch. Next to me sat Milton Speiser. I felt uncomfortable sitting next to him. Milt's father was president of a bank. Milt was old—fifteen, anyhow. His clothes, even his hiking clothes, looked like the kind you'd only wear on a special holiday.

And then I saw his sandwiches! Cucumber sandwiches. Tiny white squares, held elegantly, with the little finger crooked.

I was as ashamed of Mother's sandwiches as I sometimes was of Father's beard.

I fed my mouth with Mother's sandwiches, the way a butcher stuffs meat into a grinding machine. I didn't chew; I only swallowed. I couldn't bear that Milt or any of the other fellows should see my big, awkward sandwiches. I got them out of sight quickly. I hid them inside me.

For weeks after that awful experience I wondered if Mother's sandwiches were so very big because we were so very poor. It struck me as a paradox, however; poverty should make sandwiches small, not big. But Milt's sandwiches were tiny, and he was rich—his father was a banker.

I decided we were definitely poor, not just in the middle. I started searching for corroborative proof.

Mother kept fruit, cake, and strudel—things like that—locked in the massive sideboard in our dining room. It was Father who said it was massive. Massive furniture "looked like something." That was what Father liked.

The massive sideboard had two swinging doors. Mother always kept both of them locked. If just one were locked, and the other open, it didn't do any good. By putting your hand, arm, and part of your shoulder into the sideboard through the unlocked one you could reach anything in the sideboard. Mother never left one unlocked.

"We must be poor," I said to Mother, out to prove we were poor.

"If we must be, we must be," Mother said.

"Are we?"

"You said we must be."

Talking to Mother was like drinking water on a hot day; you put it in your mouth, and it came out sweat. What was the use? I went to Father.

"Why does Mother keep food locked up in the sideboard?"

Father laughed. "So you won't *nasch*, of course."

*Nasching*—eating only for the fun of it— was something I very much liked to do.

"If we were rich, I guess I could *nasch* as much as I wanted to, couldn't I?"

Father scratched his cheek where there wasn't any beard. I could tell he knew something important was bothering me.

"You asked me before," he said, "whether we were poor or rich. What is it, Willie? Tell me. Aren't you happy?"

"Oh, sure!"

Dainty cucumber sandwiches appeared in my mind. Father scrubbing a kitchen floor came next. And then I thought, Milt's father, Mr. Speiser, wouldn't scrub a kitchen floor. Rich men don't do things like that. Poor Father must be poor.

Poor Father had picked up a book and was reading. I felt awfully sorry for poor Father. If I could become heavyweight champion of the world by knocking out Jack Dempsey, then Father wouldn't scrub floors anymore, and the swinging doors on the sideboard could remain unlocked.

I started to go outside, but Father called to me, walked toward me with the book in his hand. It was a big red one, one from a set.

"You know what Emerson said, Willie?" Father found a line on the page with his forefinger, ran it along the line as he read. " 'Things are in the saddle and ride mankind.' You understand that?"

"What kind of things?"

"Material things. Things that aren't spiritual."

"Like ice-cream cones. But that's silly. How could an ice-cream cone . . ."

Father interrupted me. Slowly, patiently he explained what Emerson meant. I could tell he thought it was important that I understand what Emerson meant. Father always explained things to me that way. He was "bringing me up right."

"To bring children up right," Father said time and time again, "and make men of them in the fullest sense of the term is a great responsibility."

After this talk I tried—unsuccessfully—to convince myself that the things of the spirit were more important than wanting a lot of things with which you could have fun.

Just the same, I did forget all about whether we were rich or poor.

It was over two years before I remembered I'd even thought about it.

One morning there was a headline in the *Times Recorder*. Tall, real black letters. SPEISER CHARGED WITH EMBEZZLEMENT.

There was a fellow at school who had the paper. A whole group was looking at it.

"Milt's old man did a Jesse James," someone said.

"I'd like to work in a bank. Hundred-dollar bills all around. Wow!"

"They work hard in banks. When they close in the afternoon, that's when they really get working. My brother knows a guy who's teller in the First National . . ."

Though I was listening to all this talk, I was thinking of Milt Speiser. I was putting myself in his place. But putting Father in a striped prison suit was too ludicrous to visualize for more than a second.

I was surprised that Milt came to school that morning as if nothing was wrong. I kept looking at him, wondering what he was thinking. He must be terribly worried, I thought. I know I'd be.

But if Mr. Speiser was rich, why did he steal? It didn't make sense. If he were poor and stole, it would have made more sense. It was as crazy as those big sandwiches that time, a long time ago, making me feel poor, when they should have made me feel just the opposite.

"Well," I decided, "I'll have to talk to Father about it."

Before I got around to it, I met Dr. Scott on the street one day. He asked me how I was and how Father was.

"All right," I said.

He laughed. "Well, that means no business for me."

And then he started telling me what a lucky boy I was to have Father for a father. He finished by saying that as far as he knew, Father was the only Christian in town, and that if Christ were around he would be chummy with Father.

"But my father's not a Christian," I told Dr. Scott, feeling the need to set him straight. "He's Jewish."

Dr. Scott put his hand around my muscle and squeezed it. "Maybe your dad is Jewish," he said. "But just the same, he's the best Christian in this town. And likely the only one. Don't you forget it."

I didn't. Because I was sure Dr. Scott was wrong about Father's being a Christian.

Then one day Conroy, who used to take the furnace ashes out of our cellar and who always tried to measure the length of my nose by putting his forefinger alongside it, asked Father, "Is it true the last words in the Bible are 'Get the money'?"

Father acted like he was taking Conroy seriously. "Oh, no," Father said. "The Bible's last word is 'Love thy neighbor.' "

170

But Father knew what Conroy meant.

And I recalled what Dr. Scott had said about Father being a Christian.

And on another day I saw a book among Father's books. It was a very little book, and it had blue satin covers—almost like silk.

The name of the book was *The Imitation of Christ,* and it was by Thomas à Kempis. I again recalled what Dr. Scott had said about Father, and I wondered if Father had been reading this book.

I opened up the book and looked inside it. I didn't read anything; I just looked at it. And I wondered some more.

# ❧❧❧❧❧❧❧ELEVEN❧❧❧❧❧❧

To Father, the world and Zanesville, Ohio, were synonymous. It was his personal microcosm. Sy said that. When he said it, I went to the dictionary and looked up microcosm.

Zanesville was a wonderful place to all of Father's children, too.

The Terrace was a section of town to be looked at with wide, gulping eyes. You had to cross a bridge—the Monroe, the Fifth Street or the Y bridge—to get to it. Putnam was also a section of town that required bridge crossing to reach, but it lacked the Terrace's opulent stature. There were bigger houses in the Terrace, lolling in luxury on more spacious lawns.

Many of the houses in the Terrace had fruit trees, on side lawn or back yard. The people were so rich in the Terrace they didn't bother to eat the fruit from their trees; the fruit just fell, lay on the ground.

If one were fast, one could acquire some of that fruit.

Sophie, Dave, Bob, Mott, Sy, and I were fast enough.

Father said it was a shame and disgrace—our being fast enough.

But Mother said, "If someone doesn't take it, it'll just rot there on the ground."

"Well," Father said with thoughtful hesitancy, "it certainly isn't right that such good fruit should go to waste. There are always hungry people. Food shouldn't go to waste . . ."

After that, when we'd dart under a tree in the Terrace and dart away again with some fruit, we felt we were being very religious.

A good place to carry fruit was inside your shirt. If you had enough to go all the way around, it looked as if you were wearing a life belt.

But the Terrace was only one of Zanesville's many wonders.

There was Mr. Papendulis's shoeshine parlor at the corner of Seventh and Main streets. I was fascinated by a sign on the wall. It said:

> I had a friend and I did trust him.
> I lost my friend and lost his custom.
> To lose my friend did grieve me sore,
> So I resolved to trust no more.

For a long time, I felt sorry for Mr. Papendulis. Not just that he lost his friend, but that a hard cynicism had come with that loss. Besides, Mr. Papendulis seemed like such a foreigner, and to be so thoroughly foreign must, I felt, be most unpleasant.

Near the sign about losing his friend were three pictures. Two were of battle scenes in a Greek war, and one was of a Greek king.

Mr. Sam Shushish wasn't Greek; he was an Arab. And he seemed much happier than Mr. Papendulis. Of course he had reason to be. He sold ice cream, candy, and fruit, and that was quite different than shining shoes.

Mr. Shushish's store was on upper Main Street. It smelled like the inside of our sideboard —where Mother kept all the things locked up she didn't want us to *nasch* between meals.

Mr. Shushish always wore a white apron, and it was very white because it was so completely clean.

The tables in the back of his store had marble tops, and their legs were made of wire. The chairs had wire legs, too, and wire backs— wooden seats, though.

In the summertime, there were a lot of electric fans that kept you cool and that threw all the wonderful smells all around.

To sit in Mr. Sam Shushish's store with the fans going, the smells hitting you, your mouth filled with ice cream your tongue played with and detained, was the best thing that could possibly happen to you.

Mr. Shushish didn't stand up straight when he walked. He leaned backwards; his stomach and white apron preceded him. No wonder he smiled and was so happy. He never had to step out of his store; he could stay there all the time. I couldn't; I had to go home.

But nothing in Zanesville was uninteresting, so it wasn't too bad leaving Mr. Sam Shushish's store.

In the spring, there were violets under the Monroe Street bridge. You could pick as many as you wanted—for nothing.

At the top of Spring Street there was a watering trough. When a horse became thi    it was brought there for a drink. I often wor   ed how you could tell when a horse was thirs /.

It was fun to watch the horses drink. They sucked up the water, gallons and gallons of it. But they had big bellies, I reasoned, and it t a lot of water to fill them.

The trough had moss inside it. Stringy and beautifully green. If mermaids have hair, this was the kind of hair, I was sure, they must have.

Once Dave put his mouth down into the water of the trough.

He brought his head up and yelled at me. "Hey!" he yelled. "I'm a horse!"

Water dripped down from Dave's mouth, just the way it did from the horses' mouths.

I thought it might be very good being a horse, for a while; sucking your naked belly full of water from that trough.

And Zanesville was the birthplace of Zane Grey, the writer.

It had the only Y bridge in the world.

I was determined to believe this was true, though there was talk that there was also a bridge in Turkey that was in the shape of the letter Y.

There were the tile works and the potteries. Moxahala Park, that was named after an Indian and that you had to ride on an interurban to get to. Two opera houses, the Schultz and the Weller's. And more moving-picture shows than you could ever afford to see.

Yet in spite of all these wonders, wonders enhanced by childhood, Dave and Soph and Bob and I were all eager to leave Zanesville. Father had had a pulpit offered him in Terre Haute, Indiana.

"You think I want to leave Zanesville?" Father said, sorrowfully. "I'd be happy to stay here for the rest of my life."

But Terre Haute wanted to pay Father $3,000 a year. Mother, therefore, decided that contentment was a luxury Father couldn't afford. Sy at this time was getting a master's degree in mathematics at Columbia. And Mott was studying dairy farming at an agricultural school. But Mother wanted all her children to go to college and "be something," and she wanted Father to take care of the bill.

So when it came right down to it, Father was the only one who didn't want to leave Zanesville. Mott and Sy weren't involved, because they weren't home. Counting Mother, Father was out-numbered five to one.

Father was terribly smart, however, and I was worried.

The scheme that would persuade Father to go to Terre Haute occurred to me the day I had my palm read for a penny.

There was a machine on South Sixth Street that told your fortune. There was a place to put your hand, a slot for the penny. The card that came out revealed what your hand had revealed to the machine.

"Look," I said to Bob and Dave, "if we can get a card out of that machine that says we ought to move, and I show it to Father, maybe he'll want to leave town."

"How do you know there's a card in there that says somebody ought to move?" Bob wanted to know.

And Dave said the idea was good, but it sounded expensive to him.

"Well, don't you want to go to Terre Haute?" My tone was consciously irritable, impatient. I had to get money out of them. "Isn't it worth three cents to each of you to be able to get out of this town?"

Four pennies went into the slot. Sophie, Bob, Dave, and a kid we picked up in the street had their fortunes told, but not a single card said anything about moving.

Then Sophie had an idea. Allison McGregor,

a girl in her room at school, had told her that as soon as school was out, in June, her family was going to move to Bexley, just outside of Columbus.

"Well, maybe if we got her to have her fortune told," Sophie concluded excitedly, "maybe we'd have a card that said something about moving. And then we could show it to Father, and then . . ."

"Gosh, you're stupid as a pineapple!" Dave shouted. "You think that thing tells your fortune?"

"Look what it says about me," Sophie protested. "Look how right it is about me."

"Stupid. Is there one girl in the whole world who doesn't like pretty clothes? That's not fortune-telling."

Just the same, Sophie produced Allison McGregor who had freckles across her nose and a green ribbon in her red hair and skinny legs that were as white as milk.

Allison put her hand on the machine. I put the penny into the slot. The card came out.

Sophie grabbed it and started reading it to herself, mumbling, but then she started to laugh and jump up and down. "Listen!" she squealed with delight. "Just listen!"

"We're listening."

"Will you go ahead and read it?"

" 'The trip you are contemplating taking,' " Sophie read, " 'will make a profound change in your life that you will never regret. Remember, nothing ventured, nothing gained.' "

Five pennies and coincidence gave us this wonderful card to show to Father—and made us firm believers in the fortune-telling machine.

We believed in the machine to the extent of picking Bob to give the card to Father, presenting it as his own fortune. We picked Bob because the machine's fortune for Bob had said people believed in him.

Father laughed, handed back the card to B , Allison M Gregor's card. "Nonsense," Father said. "Sur ly you don't believe in such nonsense."

We were so earnest in proclaiming our trust in the machine that Father became very serious and said he would have to show us how wrong we were. He was about to go to the library anyway, so he walked up to South Sixth Street with us.

On the way, I figured out why Father was against the machine. The Bible was against divination and magic, that was why.

"How about Moses and his brother Aaron?" I thought. "Look at the tricks they did. Turning a rod into a snake and all that kind of thing."

"Moses and Aaron had no choice," Father would probably say to that. "They had to fight magic with magic. The Egyptians started it, so they had to go ahead and finish it."

You had to think things out before you said them to Father. You just gave your tongue extra futile work if you didn't think things out first.

Father made short work of the fortune-telling machine. First he put the book he was returning to the library on the machine instead of his hand, and a card came out with a fortune for the book, advising the book to study dancing since it possessed innate grace. Father then put the back of his hand on the machine and not his palm as he was supposed to, but a fortune came out just the same.

We protested that Father wasn't being fair to the machine.

"All right then," Father said, "I'll do exactly as I'm supposed to do."

By this time the machine had come to the end of its repertoire; it disgorged a fortune for Father that said he liked pretty clothes. It was the same fortune Sophie had received. And you could say very definitely—without fear of error—that Father wasn't at all interested in pretty clothes.

Though I was disappointed in the fortune-telling machine for letting us down, I was equally disappointed in Father. Why couldn't he be as excited about going to another city as I was? As Dave and Bob and Sophie were?

A new city would be filled with stores and streets and movie houses I had never seen before. It would be like a gift you unwrapped as fast as you could in order to see.

And Zanesville had a population of 30,000. Terre Haute had 75,000. That was more than twice as much. This fact alone, to my way of thinking, was enough to make one want to trade one for the other. It certainly worked that way with candy. Who wouldn't trade ten jawbreakers for twenty jawbreakers?

Though I didn't try to sway Father with this analogy, he finally decided to leave Zanesville and go to Terre Haute. It was Mother and her money-for-college argument that finally persuaded him.

The last thing he did before leaving Zanesville was to get old Joe Whatchamacallit a job. Joe Whatchamacallit's name wasn't just Polish; it was long and Polish. Kopankiewiczo. Whatchamacallit was easier to say. After twenty years of work in the tube works out in Putnam, he was fired.

Joe Whatchamacallit had a long mustache. It measured seven and a half inches from end to end. He never wore a tie; just kept his shirt collar buttoned. He came to Father when he lost his job. He put on a new shirt for the occasion, but no tie, just the shirt collar buttoned.

Joe Whatchamacallit's long mustache was gray, and he was peasant short, hardly five feet tall.

I think Father felt worse about Joe Whatchamacallit's being fired than Joe Whatchamacallit did himself—just as bad, anyhow.

"Don't you bother your head," Father said to Joe Whatchamacallit. "I'll see what I can do."

"But you're going from town right away, no, Rabbi?"

"First, I'll see what I can do," Father said. "There are always trains. The railroad doesn't run out of trains."

I was worried. If Father didn't get Joe Whatchamacallit a job, we might be held up in Zanesville indefinitely. I wondered if he was going to pray for a job, the way he prayed for Joel Bernstein's life. Father's prayers ought to be able to produce a job fairly easily. A job was simple compared to somebody's life.

Father got Mr. Joe Whatchamacallit a job as a street cleaner. He thought that that would be just the job for Joe Whatchamacallit. The idea came to him when he saw a man clean the Fifth Street bridge of what the horses left as they passed.

Father didn't pray this time. He went to see Mayor Crawford, saw him in his florist shop, and talked him into having Joe Whatchamacallit take care of the bridge that went over to Putnam. If the Fifth Street bridge needed one man to take care of it, so did the bridge that went over to Putnam. There were just as many horses passing over to Putnam. The mayor could see that Father was perfectly right.

Joe Whatchamacallit was at our house the night of the farewell gathering. So was big and ugly Leone Wexler, old man Deevers the fireman, Joel Bernstein and his mother—and all the others Father had helped. There were a lot of people at our house. People in just about every room—downstairs, that is.

The congregation presented Father with a monogrammed gold charm for him to wear on his watch chain. It could open up like a locket. It was round and there were places for two round pictures. Father never put pictures in it, and he called it a lavaliere.

The next day when 've went to the train, I could see that Father w; very sad, for he was so very quiet.

When Mother said he looked as if 'd just tasted an egg that once was fresh, Father answered, "How can I possibly feel joy at leaving Zanesville? How?"

"Is it just because they gave you that thing for your watch chain?" I asked.

Father said it wasn't that in itself, but all that the presentation of the lavaliere implied. I reminded Father then about his views on enjoyment. According to what he'd said in the past, he should be enjoying leaving Zanesville just as much as if he were remaining there.

Once at a picnic, while everyone was having a good time eating and drinking too much, Father said, and it sounded just like Father in his sermons, "All our life should be just like this," he said. "Pleasant. Happy. We should not say, 'As soon as such and such happens, I'll really enjoy life,' we should enjoy life even before such and such happens, because such and such may never happen. We must practice enjoying every moment, become expert at it. Because if we don't practice we won't be able to enjoy even that which should be very easy for us to enjoy. To become experts at enjoyment is important. Not just the enjoyment of big things, but of little things, every little thing. Here's a meal, enjoy it terribly. There's a bird flying, let the sun striking its wings send you into ecstasy."

Father stopped talking, because a baby started howling. The baby had fallen into the wash tub filled with soft drinks, ice, and melted ice. It howled even after it was fished out.

"Enjoy that, Rabbi!" someone challenged, and everybody laughed and everybody did enjoy it.

Father couldn't have enjoyed our arrival in Terre Haute any more than I did.

I was surprised Terre Haute wasn't hilly like Zanesville was. Father had told me Terre Haute was French for "high land," but someone who didn't know the French language very well must have given the city its name.

Father called on the president of the congregation first; his next stop was the synagogue. He was very anxious to see the synagogue.

It was massive. It was made of pressed brick. It had an inside toilet.

## TWELVE

I was fifteen when I announced to Father that I was going to become a professional fighter. He looked at me for a long time.

"We'll see," he said, finally.

"What do you mean?" I asked worriedly.

Father's "we'll see" sounded an awful lot like "nothing will come of all this, so why should I get myself excited and Willie excited by telling him that I refuse to permit him to be a fighter?"

"We'll see," Father said again, irritably this time. "We'll see."

I left Father's study. There was no use talking to him if he was just going to say "we'll see" and nothing else. But I decided as I walked that I would be a fighter and that nothing, nothing, *absolutely nothing* would stop me from fighting and becoming champion of the world. My eyes were so blurred with the tears that suddenly filled my eyes that I could hardly see the dining-room table in front of me. The dining-room table wobbled with distortions.

"Willie."

I turned, sniffed twice in an attempt to clear my eyes of tears.

"Come back," Father said. "Come back, Willie. I want to talk to you."

I walked back into the study, hoping Father couldn't tell there had been tears in my eyes. I didn't say anything. Father didn't say anything either. We just stood there. And then I felt alarm. Father was about to use his fine mind on me. I could tell.

"I'm going to be a fighter!" I said, so loud it was almost a shout. "So there's no use—no use at all—your trying to stop me."

"Am I trying to stop you?"

"I can tell."

Father opened his eyes wide. He always did that when he wanted to show that he was innocent. And it always made him look more guilty than ever.

"You said, 'We'll see.' Not 'All right.'"

Father smiled. I understood his smile, just as I understood his wide-opened eyes. It was a patience-and-understanding smile.

Father asked me to tell him all about it from the beginning. I told him that even back in Zanesville I'd decided I was going to be a fighter. Joey Wallace, Zanesville's sensational welterweight, had inspired me. I'd seen him on Zanesville's streets, followed him to be able to look at him longer. And I reminded Father that he often said he would not interfere with his children's day I was terribly disappointed in Father. I'd happened to eavesdrop on this subterfuge, because I'd been so eager to learn what Mother's reaction would be. Then, because of what Father said, I was sorry I'd listened.

Underneath my disappointment in Father ran the realization that he was doing what he thought "best" for me. I turned from this realization, however; I didn't want to see or acknowledge it.

I made the Wiley High School boxing team.

Next, I was determined to show Father that a few punches weren't going to discourage me.

We had only one match, that against Terre Haute's other high school, Garfield.

Garfield High's star was John L. Sullivan. It was his real name. And he was my opponent.

Before weighing-in time, I walked and walked. *John L. Sullivan.* Anyone with such a name, I thought, must be a wonderful fighter. His father and mother must be fight fans to have given him such a name. They must have started teaching him how to box as soon as they'd finished teaching him how to sit up in a high chair.

I walked and walked; I wanted to be sure and make the weight, and thinking about John L. Sullivan, my opponent, was easier while walking than while standing still or sitting down.

I weighed in at 111¼ because of all that walking; 115 was the weight at which I was fighting.

I tried my best to talk Father into going to the fight.

"How could I watch somebody hitting you?" he asked.

"You wouldn't have to," I answered, with a confidence that was purely assumed. "I'm going to do all the hitting."

It so happened I did.

The fight was stopped after the second round, and I won on a technical knockout. John L. Sullivan wouldn't come out for the third round. He just sat in his corner and cried—like a real baby.

In spite of the crying, which dampened the edge of my victory, my victory was wonderful. I was so happy, I was sure I could never be any happier.

Just the same, I still had the job of convincing Father that fighting was all right. I'll take him to a fight, I decided one day. He's never seen a fight; he should at least see a fight.

It was as Mother said so often, "You shouldn't say a cake is no good before it's even in the oven."

And since Father wouldn't see me being hit, but two unknowns hitting each other, it would be all right. I had no idea at the time, of course, that circumstance was going to make me a participant in the first and last fight Father ever attended.

I'd saved up enough money for two seats up in

the pigeon roost, but Father said he would buy his own ticket.

"I want to see what this fighting business is like," Father said. "I'm actually glad you talked me into going. So I'll buy my ticket. It's for my edification, after all, that we're going. We'll say nothing to Mother, because what she doesn't know won't hurt us."

I felt very self-conscious when Father walked into the lobby of the Grand Opera House with me. It was crowded with groups of people, and all of them were talking fast and loud. Father's beard—and Father—were out of place there. Fight fans just didn't wear beards.

Father bought his ticket, but before I reached the box office who should come up to me but Mr. Savage. Mr. Savage was the trainer of Wiley High School's boxing team. Some fellows called him Danny—that was his first name—but I always called him Mr. Savage. I tried to call him Danny, but I couldn't. He was short and had one cauliflower ear; it was cauliflowered neatly; it didn't stick out or lop over, but was just filled up. I looked at his ear a lot. I wished I had a neat cauliflower ear like Mr. Savage. It was neat, and people would be able to tell right away, without your even telling them, that you were a fighter.

Mr. Savage grabbed my arm and pulled me out of the crowd, inching its way up to the ticket seller.

"Gotta talk to yuh, kid," he said.

191

I looked back, but I couldn't see Father because of the crowd. But by the time we came to an uncrowded spot in the lobby Father came up to us.

"This your old man?" Mr. Savage said, and before I could say anything he grabbed Father's hand. "Glad to meetcha," he said. "Billy here's got a great left hand. He's a comer. A natural."

Father looked bewildered, the way he looked when he went into the chicken coop to catch a chicken and chickens flew all around him.

"How yuh feel, Billy?" Mr. Savage asked me.

All I was able to do was smile weakly and nod.

"Yuh can go six," Mr. Savage said. "Your wind's good, an' your legs're okay. And I'm sure you can take this Toughie Nolan. I wouldn't be puttin' yuh in there if I didn't think you could take him."

"You don't mean you want Willie—Billy—to perform *tonight?*" Father asked Mr. Savage, and his face still had that bewildered look.

"Sure. I'll fix it up in no time. The lad Toughie was supposed to go on with busted his right mitt in trainin' ."

I could see Father didn't understand many of the words Mr. Savage was using so fluently and so vigorously.

"The lad wires in from South Bend a couple of hours ago about his mitt. So they got no one to go on with Toughie. I think of the kid right away. With that left hand of his . . ."

Father didn't have a chance to protest; Mr. Savage talked too fast. Father might have been somewhat frightened, too, for there was something fierce about Mr. Savage's staccato speech and his gestures that sliced the air with the side of his hand. And then there was Mr. Savage's cauliflower ear, even though it was neat.

As for myself, I was too much in awe of Mr. Savage even to begin to say what I was thinking.

And I was scared—to the trembling point. I was being taken, led, to fight Toughie Nolan. Just a mere week ago I had seen Toughie knock out Sailor Maxwell, knock him out cold in the first minute of fighting.

Suddenly I was in a dressing room. I remembered leaving Father, going through the stage door, walking down cavelike corridors; but it was all very vague and unreal as though remembered through mist.

While Mr. Savage was taping my hands, Toughie Nolan and his manager, Lou Brickley, and a couple of other men came into the dressing room. The room was no bigger than a packing box, so it was very full now.

Lou Brickley was long and thin as spaghetti, and there was a derby on top of his little head that kept his monkey face in shadow. He said Toughie would go easy with me, carry me along for the six rounds. He put his hand on my bare shoulder and smiled. It was like the smile of the worst villain in a moving-picture serial.

"Just don't get too smart, Billy," he said. "And nobody'll get hurt. You see?"

Mr. Savage didn't say anything. I wanted him to, but he didn't. This was fixing a fight. This was crooked.

Father said an occupation—any occupation— was all right as long as it was honest and useful. What would he say about this? I knew what he would say. But I couldn't force myself to say what he would say.

Toughie Nolan—for one thing, the main thing—was standing there, a towel over his shoulders. The towel didn't cover his biceps or his forearms. Veins were a network of bas-relief all over them. And on his right forearm there was a tattooed heart. It was the color of canned salmon and diagonally across it, in blue, were the words Sweet Sue.

The veins made Toughie Nolan appear very powerful; the tattooing, old and worldly wise.

How could I say to him and to his manager, Lou Brickley, "You don't have to go easy with me. This fight has got to be honest. And I don't want you to think for a minute that I can't take care of myself."

I was only fifteen and being in a dressing room, a dressing room in the Grand Opera House, a dressing room with Toughie Nolan and his manager and Mr. Savage, filled me with such awe that I wasn't capable of saying one word, any word.

didn't get too smart. And not letting Toughie hit me was being "too smart." But I couldn't let him hit me, because if Father was out there in the darkness, he couldn't stand seeing me hit.

I kept jabbing Toughie's face. They weren't hard punches because I was thinking of Lou Brickley—I'd surely hurt Lou Brickley's feelings if I hit Toughie hard.

Toughie came tearing after me. I stepped lightly to one side and he went roaring by.

The tumult out in the darkness turned to laughter.

Out of the laughter, a voice screeched, "Eat 'im up, Billy! Eat 'im up!"

Furiously angry, Toughie charged. My left went out, reflexively. The power of the blow was multiplied many times by the force of Toughie's charge.

There was Toughie's face. The angry lines in it were gone. Its blond redness had turned pale. It was a stupid, pale, dazed face.

My left hand shot out a half dozen times, and hit the face a half dozen times. And then Toughie went down, the way smoke goes up, slowly, gracefully.

What followed was a blur of excitement. The referee didn't bother to count Toughie out; he was very concerned in getting him onto the stool in his corner. I tried to help him. I felt sorry for Toughie. I couldn't help putting myself in Toughie's place, for Father had me in the habit of putting myself in the other fellow's place. What if Toughie, I asked myself, had knocked me out?

It was too horrible even for conjecture.

Father was waiting for me out in front of the Grand Opera House. As I came toward him, I wondered if it wouldn't have been better, from Father's point of view, if I hadn't won so decisively.

What if he thought fighting was brutal? He m ht.

' low is Toughie?" Father said before he said anything else.

Hearing the word Toughie come out of Father's mouth sounded strange. And he said it as though he knew Toughie very we was very concerned about him.

"He's all right," I said. "I didn't hurt him."

"You knocked him out."

"Sure, but it was just with a left jab."

I was trying to make professional boxing seem as genteel as I possibly could, so Father wouldn't be against my continuing in the fight game.

"Where is Mr. Savage who was so good as to attend you in the ring?" Father asked.

"And he's a great second, too. He's back there talking to Toughie's manager. He said . . ."

"You're very good at this sort of thing," Father said, as we stood waiting for a car to go by so that we could cross the street. "You know with whom the people in the audience were comparing you? With Benny Leonard. You apparently use your left arm the way he did. Many of them were saying that you're a replica of Benny Leonard."

"Is that what they said?"

I was terribly happy, not because the fight fans thought I was a second Benny Leonard, but because Father had heard them express that view. Father had a big thick book at home about the Jew in America and his contribution to the sciences, art, and culture of America. Benny Leonard was in that book.

"They say all you must learn," Father went on to say, "is how to use your right arm."

"I'll learn to use it," I said. "And I'll do a lot for America."

Father started to hum a Hebrew tune, and I knew he was thinking.

"As I watched the behavior of the people in the audience," Father said, "I thought of William James and what he had to say concerning a moral equivalent for war."

I wasn't listening to Father now; my mind was too full of my victory over Toughie Nolan, and my going on and becoming a champion. Father's voice was like the unheard mumble of the referee before my fight.

But Father went on talking about William James. You wouldn't think that anyone would talk about William James after a fight. But that's the way Father was.

# ❧❧❧THIRTEEN❧❧❧

SINCE Father was a rabbi, he shouldn't have enjoyed my boxing career, but he did.

He liked to see my name in huge letters on the boxing cards. He liked the way people I did not even know called me Billy—people walking in the street.

Only one conce    marred his pleasure. I might injure my opponent.

"Can't you win more easily, gently?" Father would ask.

Father was trying to say that it was all right for me to win, but I really shouldn't kayo my opponent.

But it seemed that Mother didn't care what I might do to my opponents, she was only apprehensive about what they might do to me. And she worried about my not being strong enough to box, since I didn't eat meat. Mother, I decided once again, was different from Father. And I supposed—with a trace of resignation— that a mother couldn't help acting like a mother.

She'd acted like a mother, for example, when my brother Mott had left home to be a farmer.

She'd said he'd gone off to dig in the mud.

Father said farming was among the noble professions. The only reason I didn't like it was that it kept Mott from home. He'd been away from home so much, all I vividly remembered about him was the wide space between his front teeth—he could spit through that space or use it for whistling.

Mother went right on worrying about Mott. She was sure that when he wasn't digging in the mud, he was carrying terribly heavy sacks on his back.

"You're so worried about me," I once said to Mother, "I should think you'd be worried about all the fellows I fight."

"I've plenty, *plenty* to do just worrying about you. Let the other fellow's mother worry about her son."

"Do you have to worry?"

"Yes," Mother answered simply, helplessly.

"If you realized how I'm beginning to get that right hand over in the good old one-two, maybe you wouldn't worry so much."

"Willie," Mother said with sad pleading, "can't you get out of that *bummerischa* business?"

*Bummerischa* was an adjective meaning fit for a bum.

"You're a woman," I said. "That's the trouble with you. If you were a man, you wouldn't worry so much and you'd be able to understand how I feel . . ."

201

"Your father's against your fighting. He's a man."

"He's not against it the way you are."

"What difference does it make how he's against it? He's against it. That's the main thing."

"Aw, what's the use!" I said.

"Someday you'll say, 'Mother was right. I should have listened to my mother.'"

"Sure. Sure."

"You get your nose hurt, your lips cut, your eyes black and blue. And how does it look that the rabbi's son . . ."

I left the kitchen and Mother's argument. I felt like a martyr. The feeling was familiar, but I still found it pleasant.

Father didn't argue with me the way Mother did. He believed in "influencing" people.

And he, finally, caused me to give up boxing by "influencing" me.

You could influence people—according to Father's method—by not saying a word.

There was the time Father and I were on a crowded street car. We had to stand up, and next to us, also standing, was a tall, skinny woman. One person left the car, and so there was an empty space on the benchlike seat, but the tall, skinny woman wouldn't take it.

Father smiled and said, "Won't you be seated?"

The tall, skinny woman's lips were very thin

and purple. She had her mouth shut so tightly as she shook her head that you could hardly see her purple lips.

But I could see she didn't want to sit down because she'd have to sit down next to a Chinese. I'd heard about such things—only heard about them. I could tell by the pale way Father looked that I was right; this was one of them.

Father got busy right away "influencing" the tall, skinny woman. There was room for the tall, skinny woman on the seat, but there wasn't nearly enough room for Father because he was short and fat.

Father sat down next to the Chinese.

He had to sit on the sharp edge of the seat and be careful that he didn't slide off, but he sat there.

And Father talked to the Chinese as if he'd known him for a long long time. The Chinese didn't say very much, but he smiled an awful lot. He smiled all the time—steadily.

I kept my eyes on the face of the tall, skinny woman. I was looking for some sign that the influencing was taking effect. I couldn't tell; she kept on looking exactly the same. I was disappointed.

When Father and I had left the street car, I said to Father, "She didn't want to sit down, did she?"

"No," Father said.

"There was loads of room for her because she was tall and skinny."

"Perhaps she wanted to stand," Father said. "Perhaps she had been sitting down all day."

I studied Father's face.

"Perhaps," I said.

I knew Father wouldn't say the real reason why the tall skinny woman wouldn't sit down; he didn't believe in saying anything bad about anyone. He agreed with Plato, the philosopher.

Once at the dinner table, he didn't do anything but talk about Plato and what a wonderful man he was. Father was all excited, in just the way Sy was the day he learned how food is digested in the stomach.

According to Father, Plato believed that people did the wrong thing only when they didn't know what the right thing was. And therefore, Father concluded, people couldn't be blamed.

Mother had a ready answer for Plato's and Father's argument. "Ignorance of the law is no excuse," she stated, clipping off the words nice and close.

"But this is moral law that we're speaking of," Father objected. "And that's entirely different from the—the law of the courtroom."

"I wonder if it is," Mother said.

Father stopped his soup spoon halfway through the cold potato in his hot borscht. "Do you want to make nothing of Plato?" Father asked Mother.

"I've nothing against Plato," Mother said.

"But why must you always search to find excuses for the bad behavior of bad people?"

"People try to be happy. They try very hard. They make mistakes. Life isn't as certain as your *lockshen kugel.*"

Father's reference to the infallible perfection of mother's *lockshen kugel,* a most delicious blend of noodles, nuts, raisins and apples, produced a bright light in Mother's eyes. Flatter Mother's cooking and she turned to ice cream in the sun.

Father saw that Mother could offer no resistance now. He pushed his chair back from the dinner table and continued, exactly as if he were in the synagogue, delivering a sermon.

"Do you think there is a man alive who wants to be greedy or jealous or hateful? Is there a woman who—who desires coarseness of behavior? Certainly not. They want to be good—in the all-inclusive meaning of that term. They want to be beautiful and noble and fine. They . . ."

"Certainly," Mother said, "everyone tries to do the best they can. I know that. So finish your soup. It'll get cold."

When we'd finished dinner, Father said to me, "Let's sit on the porch and rest up."

Father always liked to rest up after a meal. He didn't eat any more than I, and compared with me he had much more room in which to put food, but still he liked to rest up after a meal.

I looked at Father as he sat beside me rocking on the porch.

"I'll bet Father's greater than Plato," I thought. "Plato had a beard, too. But there are plenty of people who have beards, and they're not very great."

Both of Father's hands were on his vest. There weren't any wrinkles in Father's vest. After dinner his vest was filled so tight there weren't any wrinkles in it.

Father wasn't rocking now. His chin was down on his bow tie, and his eyes were closed. His breathing was louder, but not as loud as snoring.

I swung both my legs over the arm of my rocker. Relaxed—my head against the back of the rocker—I studied Father. Beard. Skull cap. Profile. The hand that sleep had taken away from his vest, hanging so its fingers almost touched the floor.

"You're my father," I said aloud, incredulously, proudly, and as though by compulsion. "There you are. My father. You're my father, and I'm your son."

I wondered if there was any other father in the whole world, besides Plato, who didn't blame anybody for what they did.

Though Father was such a very real part of me that I at times did not know where he left off and I began, still, from that day on the porch on, I found myself consciously aping him.

I remembered Father had told me, "Never be disappointed in other people; only in yourself.

206

God had felt the same way, I recalled, when He had created the heavens and the earth. The book of Genesis in the Bible said God looked upon His creations and "saw that they were good."

Off in the distance a hound was saying, "Owk, owk, owk!" And there were voices of people—distance-muted. And the sound of their voices in the spring air made me like them very deeply, though I couldn't see them and though I didn't know them.

I didn't figure out a way to help Father collect money for the new synagogue that day; I was too busy feeling, and realizing Father must feel about nature and people as I was feeling.

It was the first time I thought that maybe, because I felt about so many things the way Father felt, that maybe I ought to become a rabbi.

And I wasn't the only one in the family Father was busy "influencing" around this time.

One day Dave came home from school with a note from his teacher.

Father read the note.

"Mrs. Collins says she wants to see me," Father said to David. "What's the matter now?"

"Nothing's the matter now," David said. He could be fresh.

"Your teacher certainly doesn't want just to look at me. I'm not a beauty."

"It's nothing. It's just because I told her I wanted to be a recluse."

David's teacher, further explanation revealed,

211

had asked her pupils to tell what they were planning on being when they grew up.

She called on one student at a time.

The boys were going to be policemen, streetcar conductors, candy-storekeepers, and firemen.

The boy sitting in front of Dave said he was going to take charge of the back steering wheel of a hook-and-ladder fire truck. Then it was Dave's turn.

"I'm going to be a recluse," Dave had said.

I peeped into the living room when Mrs. Collins called on Father. Dave and Father and Mrs. Collins were in there together.

Mrs. Collins was very little; she was shorter than Father and didn't weigh nearly as much. Her bust was like a pigeon's bust.

"It's really nothing to be excited about," Father told Mrs. Collins.

But I knew Mrs. Collins. She'd been my teacher before Dave had her. She was always excited. I'd decided it was her nature.

Mrs. Collins opened her eyes wider than they were already.

"But the child said he wanted to be a recluse —that's a hermit."

Mrs. Collins walked around as she talked; she always did, because she was always excited.

Dave came to his own defense. The only reason he wanted to be a recluse, he explained, was so he would be able to devote himself to research in chemistry and physics. As a recluse, he would not be interrupted, and his discoveries would therefore be more numerous and of finer quality.

Mrs. Collins patted Dave on the hand, her hand going up and down quickly. "You filled me with a worrying spell," she said, letting go of a great sigh. "You did indeed, David. I'm so happy you're going to be a great scientist. Oh, I'm so happy. You've no idea."

When Mrs. Collins went out of the front door, and Father closed it, I went into the living room.

"Who wants to be a scientist?" Dave asked, extreme disgust accentuating his words.

"Don't you?" I asked.

"It made her happy, didn't it? My saying that. She said it made her happy. If I'd been teaching school for a hundred years like her, I'd want someone to come along and make me happy."

"If you're so concerned about her happiness," Father said, "why did you say you wanted to be a recluse?"

"If you'd been in the room and heard those kids say they were going to be policemen, one after another, or a fireman, you'd have figured out something lively to break up the disgusting monotony."

That was my brother Dave. Not so chubby now, because he was growing up and the chubbiness had gone into height.

And Sophie's pigtails were gone now. She

always wore her hair up. If you wanted to see her pigtails, you had to look at a picture Father had taken of the "children" years ago. Bob wasn't in the picture. He'd been frightened by the gruesome way the photographer's head disappeared and reappeared under the black cloth attached to the camera, and he'd run out of the studio and home. But Sophie's pigtails were in the picture, and each was tied with a bit of baby ribbon because their pictures were being taken. In embossed letters in the corner of the picture it said, Ideal Photo, South Fifth Street, Zanesville, Ohio.

And Sophie wanted to be beautiful now. After she washed her face, she rubbed her cheeks with ice. She called it a beauty treatment.

Mother said, "You're beautiful enough."

Father took Sophie's part. "You say, 'enough.' How can you set a limit to beauty?"

"I can do it," Mother declared flatly. "A girl shouldn't be too beautiful. It's not good."

"What can we do?" Father said and laughed, and squeezed one of Sophie's ice-treated cheeks between thumb and forefinger. "She's too beautiful already. She takes after her mother."

Mother went after Father then. Father laughed, the way you do when somebody tries to tickle you, and he wrapped his arms around himself for protection.

And I was growing up, too. I read Sherwood Anderson. His *Triumph of the Egg*, his *Marching Men*, his *Windy McPherson's Son*. I didn't understand most of what I read, but I read anyhow. I sensed that in these words was insight into man and the universe. It made me sad, but it was a sadness one could enjoy. And it made me feel grown-up and like Father.

Father was always saying—he never stopped—"As my son, you must set an example. Besides, you're Jewish."

For years those words were a burden just in the hearing.

Then one day—I was a senior in high school—I wished for an even greater reason to set an example.

There was a colored boy in my class whose name was Malcolm Russell. He was very tall and thin. I knew he tended furnaces before coming to school, so that he wouldn't have to quit school and work all the time. I was sure he was so thin because he had to get up early in the morning and take care of the furnaces.

And Malcolm Russell was a very serious student. He wasn't like a boy going to school; he was like an old man going to school. And his gentleness and his smile weren't the gentleness and smile of a boy, but the gentleness and smile of a grown-up person.

And he used big words in class, bigger words than anyone in high school ever used.

Once he said, "That's a strange idiosyncrasy."

The children in the classroom laughed, but Malcolm Russell's face stayed very serious.

I figured out the reason Malcolm Russell used big words was because he wanted to be cultured and as fine a person as he could possibly be. Using big words was a symbol, like Father's scrubbing the kitchen floor for old Mr. Schneller.

I once told Father about Malcolm Russell, about his being too tall and thin. About how he used big words.

"There's a big word that fits him," Father said.

"What?" I asked. "What big word?"

"Etiolation," Father said. "Do you know what it means?"

That was the difference between Father and my oldest brother Sy; Sy would use a big word and he didn't care if you knew what it meant or not. That was your lookout.

Father explained that when plants are kept out of sunlight—down in cellars, for example— they shoot up, tall and pale, and the botanists called that etiolation.

The way Father told me about etiolation made me think Father's words were like the words of Sherwood Anderson. Their words said certain things, but most important of all they made you feel a lot more.

That day in high school, when I was a senior, and after Father had told me about etiolation, I sat and looked at Malcolm Russell. My elbow was on the desk, and my cheek rested on the palm of my hand. I just sat there that way and looked at Malcolm Russell's serious face.

I felt very close to Malcolm Russell and liked him very much. The example I had to set because I was the son of a rabbi was a drop compared to the ocean of an example he had to set because his face and hands and wrists and neck weren't white. If they were white everything would be all right, because the rest of him was covered with clothes. But he might want to go in swimming. What would he do then?

I kept studying Malcolm Russell's serious face and wondered how I could really help him.

I wished I were a Negro. We'd be able to work together then, setting an example.

And if Father were one, that would be good, too.

When I thought of Father as a Negro, I thought of him without his beard. Father looked very different as a Negro—and without his beard.

Just then the teacher called on me. I took my head off the palm of my hand and sat up straight, but since I hadn't been paying attention, I hadn't heard what she had said. She was a little angry, because I hadn't been paying attention, and called on someone else.

## FOURTEEN

WHEN I decided to go to The Hebrew Union College in Cincinnati to study to be a rabbi, Father was very pleased and Mother was overjoyed. I was scared. To step from the fight ring to the pulpit—in one's thought—is after all not a tiny step.

Father said, "You'll have to get busy and prepare yourself."

I took the Bible written in Hebrew—rather, Father handed it to me—and I started right on the first page, which told about the start of all things.

"*Bereshes,* in the beginning," I translated. "*Bara Elohim,* God created. *Bereshes,* in the beginning. *Bereshes,* in the beginning. *Bara Elohim,* God created. *Es hashamayim,* the heavens. *Ves haawretz,* and the earth . . ."

With the hammer of repetition, I pounded the English translation of the Bible into my head. Word by word, repeated and repeated, until I knew the Hebrew by heart and the English by heart, and Father went around smiling even when there was nothing to smile about.

Next, Father took me to Halperin's on Main Street.

Father carried the list in his hand of the clothing I would need. Father and Mother had figured out the list the night before. They sat in the kitchen at the table, with pen and ink and paper, and figured it out. I just stood there. Listened and watched.

The suit Mr. Halperin sold me was a light blue one—the kind the storekeeper takes outside to show you how the color looks in natural light. It looked all right in natural light.

Father put his finger on the next item on the list. "Now, he should have a hat to match," he told Mr. Halperin.

"Certainly," Mr. Halperin said. "Of course." He paused and then asked, "So your boy's flying out of the nest and leaving you, huh, Rabbi?"

"That's the way it goes," Father said. "One minute, so it seems, you're teaching them to walk, and in the next they're flying away."

"There's nothing we can do about that, huh, Rabbi?"

"No," Father said. "Nothing. It's like the sun rising and setting, your children growing up and leaving you."

I didn't appreciate this conversation at all. I heard it; that was all. I was thinking about the hat I was going to get. In all my life I had never owned and worn a hat. It was either a cap, or just nothing, but never a hat.

The hat was beautiful. It was blue, the color some birds' eggs are.

"You want to take a look at it outside?" Mr. Halperin said, more to me than to Father.

I shook my head; all I wanted to do was try it on. I only hoped it would fit; there wasn't any other hat I wanted more than that hat.

Mr. Halperin helped me put it on. I'd pulled it too far back on my head—I'd never worn a hat, and this was a hat.

I stood in front of a mirror, taller than I was, and I could see my whole self, my blue suit and my blue hat.

"Now he looks like somebody," Father said, smiling proudly.

And I thought, "I look exactly like a man. It's the hat. Men wear hats."

And when we came home, Father and I, loaded down with packages, Mother said, "Put the things down, Willie. I've something for you."

"What do you mean?" I said. There was no thought in my head that she had a present for me.

She stretched out her hand toward me and there was a blue jewelry box in it, darker blue than my suit or my hat, really almost purple.

I took the box off her hand with a quick snatch, but I opened it slowly and there was a solid-gold watch; it was lying there on purple velvet.

I shut the box and handed it back to Mother

as quickly as I had taken it from her. "I don't want it," I said. "You've got to take it back."

"What's the matter with you?" Mother said. "I want you to have it."

"But it's pure gold. It must have cost an awful lot."

"How many times do you leave home?" Father said. "Take it. Don't be a little donkey."

"Take it, Willie," Mother said, stretching out her hand to me again. "Take it."

She looked as if she was going to start crying any second.

"I don't want it," I said. "I don't need it."

Tears came into my eyes, and I was crying before I knew it.

Mother put her arms around me, and she was crying, too. We were both crying. Being up against her, I was aware that she felt flat like an ironing board. And I smelled the clean soapy smell of her dress.

"It's pure gold," I sobbed. "You can't afford it. That's why I said I didn't want it."

"That's what money is for," Mother said, "to buy a gold watch for your son when he leaves home to go to college."

That didn't sound like Mother who never tired of reminding us that it was important that we know the value of a penny. It sounded more like Father.

That night I lay in bed and couldn't sleep. I just looked at the darkness of the room and thought of all the exciting things that had happened to me that day. Buying the clothes—the hat, especially—and receiving the watch from Mother. The watch was engraved all over, and on the back there was a shield and Mother said I could have my initials engraved on it. The watch had cost twenty-five dollars.

Mother loved me very much, I decided— loved me as much as Father loved me. I knew it because of the way she wanted me to have the watch. I hadn't always felt she loved me as much as Father loved me, for her love was concealed most of the time by a screen of maternal solicitude, which I knew only as orders and scoldings.

"Wash both your hands, Willie, not just one!"

"Where have you been parading around?"

"You'll grow up and live in pool rooms!"

"The night is for sleeping, not for playing!"

"Don't talk when you eat!"

"Before you cross the street, look, always look!"

Mother had become equal to the sum total of all these commands and entreaties. But I now realized she was much more than any of them or all of them, and that they were merely an expression of her true self.

The day I left for Cincinnati, a man walking toward me asked if I had the time. This was the first time anyone had asked me that. It must have been because of the blue hat. I was dressed in the blue suit and the blue hat, for at 3:05 I was to catch the train for Cincinnati.

I took out the watch Mother had given me and told him the time. I also told him that my mother had given me my watch.

He was a short man and he needed a shave and his eyes looked like frog eyes.

"You hold onto that watch," he said with a sad seriousness. "It's a good watch. Don't you ever sell it, or let anyone put their hands on it. It's a good watch."

It was plain to me he thought the watch was good solely because my mother had given it to me, because, for all he knew, it couldn't run for more than a half hour without your having to shake it to make it run again. And it was plain to me he must like his own mother very much.

Father wasn't satisfied with just taking me to the railroad station. "We should see him on his way," he said.

So everybody got in our Chevrolet, and I was escorted to Columbus, fifty-two miles away. I caught the train there.

The Columbus railroad station was very big. The one in Zanesville was a baby by comparison.

Mother kissed me good-bye.

Father kissed me, too. He kissed me quickly, because he was very bashful and kissing someone is about the worst thing a bashful person can do. His kiss was different from Mother's because of his beard and because it was quicker. I smelled his beard when he kissed me—it was a nice smell, as nice as hay, but much stronger.

223

When the train pulled out, I was sad. I felt as though I had been cut in half, and the bigger half had been left behind. I thought of Father and Mother and Bob and Dave and Sophie. They were getting in the car now, for the trip back to Zanesville. I pictured them getting into the car slowly and quietly, their thoughts still with me. And their trip back would be silent, too, all the way.

I saw the dim reflection of myself in the train window, of my blue hat. I put up both my hands and touched the rim of my hat—as though I could hardly believe it was real and right there on top of my head. Strength went from the rim of my hat through my fingers and into me. My chest lifted a little, and my shoulders went back a little.

When does being young stop? Surely by eighteen. Then old must begin.

"I'm a man," I said to myself, after this observation. "I'm taking this trip down to Cincinnati. Going to the University there. And to the seminary. I'm going to live there."

The first few months at school were exciting, but they were interlaced with homesickness, too. Father's face would float, bubble-like, between my face and the book from which I was gaining knowledge, and then I'd start thinking about home.

Father wrote to me several times a week. Get-

ting the letters and racing through them was fun,
but then I felt lonelier than before.

And then one day in December that terrible
letter came.

The envelope was like all the others. The return address in the upper left-hand corner had a
line under it—the line was broken in the middle,
and at the break Father would make two little
downward strokes with the pen.

I opened the single sheet of linen tablet paper.
Father always used linen tablet paper. I was
standing in the middle of my dormitory room—
and my roommate was out, I remember that. I
was expecting it to be just a regular letter.

I read the words on the single sheet of paper.
I was conscious of my breathing, it was getting
faster. There were just the words in blue-black
ink and my breathing and my head starting to
ache around my eyes because my mind was
straining to disbelieve the words on the paper.
That's all there was in all the world for a long,
torturing moment.

"This operation, which I must undergo,"
Father's blue-black words said, "is a very serious
one. My life is in God's hands, Willie. What will
be will be of course. You know I'm proud of you
and want you to study hard and . . ."

The words became tiny blue-black snakes,
wriggling about in the burning tears filling my
eyes.

When I reached Zanesville, and the Bethesda Hospital, the operation was over.

I half tiptoed into Father's room.

Father was very pale, a sort of a yellow pale. He looked up at me and smiled. His lips moved, but there was no voice behind the movement of his lips. The movement of his lips fitted the words, "Hello, Willie. Sit down."

There was a woman dressed all in white in the room, a nurse. "Here's a chair for you," she said, moving a chair over near the bed.

I sat down.

"Now you stay there," the nurse said, shaking her finger at Father, a smile on her very clean pink face. "I want you to be right there when I get back."

The nurse's professional joviality didn't make me less concerned about Father. I was glad when she was out of the room.

I moved to the edge of the chair, leaned forward to be closer to Father.

"How do you feel?" I asked.

Father smiled and nodded his head.

It was then I saw the green mark on Father's throat. The copper of his collar button had made it. It was always on Father's throat, under his beard.

On Friday nights, after Father had taken a hot bath and had put on a clean shirt in honor of the Sabbath, Mother helped him with his collar button and cuff links.

The round green mark on Father's throat made me want to kiss Father. But I didn't.

"I guess I better go now," I said.

Father started working to take his hand out from under the sheet. That simple act seemed so complicated and difficult for Father that I couldn't help it, I started to cry.

Father took my hand and held it; he could hardly hold it; he couldn't squeeze it.

I kissed Father then, on the cheek.

A tear was coming down my face. I caught it with my tongue.

"I'll be back later on," I said, and I backed out of Father's hospital room.

At home, Mother told me, "If he hadn't worked so hard getting the new synagogue built, he wouldn't be a sick man today."

"Why are you talking nonsense?" Sy asked. "His sickness hasn't anything to do with work. It's carcinoma. *Carcinoma.*"

Carcinoma. I didn't know what carcinoma was. It sounded like a devil with a steaming red hide and a barbed tail.

The next day I walked down to Seventh Street and looked at the new synagogue. I didn't go inside; I just stood outside. It was brand-new, as if it had just been unwrapped.

It was pressed brick, like the pressed brick of the synagogue in Terre Haute. The bricks weren't red, the color you'd expect a brick to be, but a very dark burnt-cinder sort of color.

There were steps going up to the door, and an electric light on each side of the door.

The old synagogue didn't have electricity; it had gas. And no furnace. Just two gas stoves. One on each side—one for the women, one for the men. And the isinglass windows on the gas-stove doors were always broken. It had spittoons, pottery ones, at the end of every other pew. But it didn't have an inside toilet.

"It's not modern," Father said, at least a million times.

And in the letters he wrote me, while I was in Cincinnati, he told me how modern the new synagogue was. He was especially happy about the recreation hall downstairs, and the massive oak-stained doors at the front entrance. He was working with the children on a Chanukah program for the new recreation hall when he became sick.

I looked up at the front of the synagogue. "Father didn't lay any of those pressed bricks," I thought, "but just the same he built that synagogue."

Father was capable of encompassing such paradoxes.

The days that followed were frightening days. For Father was doing very well, and Mother believed and we believed that just when people permitted their hopes to be raised about a sick person's recovery that was when that person took a turn for the worse.

It was almost as if Father's life depended on our not being fooled.

I spent a lot of time in Father's hospital room. I had a book of stories by Tolstoy that I tried to read, but my mind wandered from the book.

Whenever we "carried on" as children, Father would invariably say, "Why don't you take a book and read?"

Father believed in books. He liked to think of the Jewish people as an *Am Hasepher*—a book-reading people.

And as I sat trying to read Tolstoy, I couldn't help considering the possibility of Father's dying. Could Father possibly die? Not walk around on Zanesville's streets any more? Be gone? Dead? What if he were improving, improving couldn't always be bad. Didn't a person have to improve in order to get well?

The story by Tolstoy that I was trying to read was about a shoemaker who worked in a basement. He could see just the feet of the people who passed by his shop window. This shoemaker loved all the people who belonged to the feet that went by his shop window. He was a holy man.

Father was like that shoemaker, I thought. Exactly like him.

There was a picture of Father that was set fast in my mind, like a jewel in a ring. Father on his way home from religious school, accompanied by a half dozen of his pupils. All six tried to hold his hand as they walked. They swarmed about him. One little girl walked backwards in front of him. And Father was smiling and a little bewildered by all the attention.

I thought of the intrigue between my father and me, just the day before.

"When you come to the hospital tomorrow, Willie," Father had said, "please bring me an orange."

"But you're not supposed to eat oranges," I reminded Father.

"How can they or anyone be sure that one little orange will hurt me?"

Father had the look of a mischievous little boy. He was acting younger than I was. The way he was acting you'd think he wasn't old enough to wear a hat.

I brought Father the orange—a very little one. I'm glad I did now.

Father had so few pleasures, the pleasures that are generally recognized as pleasures.

On hot summer days he'd come home and say, "I went into a drugstore and treated myself to a bottle of soda pop." And the way he said it, you'd think he was making a confession.

I'd watched Father as he peeled the orange I'd sneaked into him. He dug the fingernail of his right thumb into the peel and peeled it.

I could never peel an orange. When I tried, the orange became all wet and messy. Father did a good dry job.

When I gave my orange to Mother to peel, she used a knife. She was always careful to get the peel off in one piece, one long inch-wide string of a piece.

Mother would have me whirl the long orange peel over my head and then let go of it. The initial the peel made was supposed to be the initial of the girl I was destined to marry.

Once I complained, "It comes out a different initial every time. How many girls am I going to marry?"

"You will have to wait and see," Mother replied.

"Well, I don't believe in the orange peels. If the orange peels were right, they would stick to one initial—or two, three at the most."

Father suggested a possibility. "Perhaps the orange peel makes the initials of the girls who will fall in love with Willie."

Mother shook her head. "No," she said, shaking her head. "The orange peel makes the initials only of girls—or boys—whom you will marry."

"Then what is wrong?" Father asked, looking worried. "Perhaps Willie doesn't whirl it correctly."

"You think I'm the only one?" I said. "The orange peel makes a different initial every time that Sophie throws . . ."

I looked at Father and Mother, and I saw that their faces were too serious, that they were straining to hold them that way, that they were really joking.

The nurse came into the room then and I put the book by Tolstoy down.

"Has he been behaving himself?" she asked me.

I looked at Father. "He's asleep," I said.

"Well, when they're asleep, they don't get into trouble. Just like you. I'll bet you don't get into trouble when you're asleep."

I didn't answer the nurse. Her blatant good spirits disturbed me. When you're around death and sickness all the time, I thought, that's the way you get. Does she think Father is going to die? Maybe that's why she's putting on this act of being cheerful.

"No," I told myself, "she's that way all the time."

Early the next morning—it was just a few minutes after six—the hospital phoned. Father was sinking fast. All of us had better come.

I didn't wait for anything or anyone. I ran all the way to the hospital. My heart was pounding so fast, and hitting my chest so hard, it felt like it was going to break through and land on the ground.

And all the way—as I ran—I felt certain that Father was going to die. I tried to bring up thoughts that would trample that certainty down, but it was no use.

When I came panting up to Father's room,

my face wet with sweat and tears, Dr. Scott stopped me at the door.

The window blind was pulled down in Father's room. A newspaper over a table lamp threw the lamp's light up against the wall and off of Father's bed. The lighting was weird, sinister.

"He's all right, isn't he?" I asked Dr. Scott. I meant, "He's not dead?" But I couldn't ask that.

Dr. Scott put his long, bony hand on my shoulder. That was the answer he was giving me to my question. Did that mean yes, or did it mean no?

"Just wait in the room directly across the corridor," he said.

I was going to ask him again if Father was all right, but then I thought he must be all right—alive—or Dr. Scott wouldn't tell me to go over there and wait.

I was the first one in that room, but pretty soon it was filled with people. I was too troubled and scared to notice who half of them were. Mr. Weiss, the president of the congregation, was there. And I couldn't help but be conscious of Mother, Mother crying quietly. And doctors and nurses coming and going, coming and going.

I kept my back to all of them and looked out of the window and cried. I didn't stop for a second; I just kept on crying and crying.

Outside the window, a thin cold rain fell. The sky was drab, gray.

When Father had improved, I was afraid he would take a turn for the worse. But this was no good either—this was terrible. That certainty that he was going to die was back in my head again. He's going to die. Can't you tell? This is what happens when people die. The nurses and the doctors walk quietly. People die this way. They have everyone across the hall and they leave you alone to die. Father's dying! He's dying!! Your father's dying!!!

I couldn't see the window or the sky; cataracts of hot tears blinded me; my throat hurt unbearably.

And then everyone started leaving the room. I felt panicky. Why is everyone leaving the room? I knew, but I tried to blot out what I knew by asking myself, "Why is everyone leaving the room?"

When I came into the corridor, I saw a nurse carrying Father's clothes. His suit that needed pressing was draped over her arm, and his black hat that was a little dusty was on top.

The clothes were so much like Father and yet they weren't Father at all, and the nurse's carrying them meant Father would never wear them again, that he was dead and finished with clothes that were life.

That was the worst thing I'd seen in all my life—the nurse carrying Father's clothes. It was worse than Shep's dying and Marvin's funeral.

It was worse than that last letter Father had written me.

The service for Father was held in the new pressed-brick synagogue.

The coffin with Father in it had been placed just below the pulpit, and a rabbi who had been sent for from Columbus conducted the service.

I didn't want to look at anyone; I looked at the floor most of the time. Still I was aware that the synagogue was packed. Not just with Jewish people. The mayor was there. And I saw old man Deevers, the fireman who used to get intoxicated, older now, time streaming down his face had gullied the wrinkles deeper. And the men didn't sit on one side and the women on the other, the way they were supposed to do in a synagogue, and I supposed it was because there were so many non-Jewish people in attendance.

In the days following the funeral, I tried to console myself by realizing that Father didn't mind dying; he took death as a part of life, rather than the end of it. The way he took it, you'd think dying was something you did every day—like going to sleep at night. But I missed him, and every time I thought that I would never see him again, I cried. I visualized him walking toward me, the fast way he walked, lifting his head inquiringly as he drew near me, and then I cried harder.

We received formal condolences from the congregation, framed and in script—just like a diploma, only much smaller. Mother hung it on the wall in the living room. Mostly, it said how wonderful Father was, and it was signed by the president of the congregation, the vice-president, and the secretary.

Legends about Father began to grow immediately. Things he had never done were ascribed to him, but they were things he might very well have done.

"He didn't have a single enemy," I heard one woman say. "After all, how could he? Before you can have an enemy, you have to be an enemy yourself."

And the woman to whom she was speaking answered, "Zanesville will never have another rabbi like him. He was a saint. A godly man."

"They don't come like that very often," the first woman said, nodding her head solemnly.

One little girl, it was reported, said she would never go to Sunday School again, not unless my Father came back and took charge.

And as I heard all these things, and felt there was so much more that I did not hear, the pain of Father's being gone was eased a bit.

I went back to Cincinnati, to school. On the train, I thought about Father a great deal. And among my thoughts was the thought that Father had set a very big example.